To Hope

FRIENDS FOREVER

FRIENDS FOREVER

By
Alix Hurd

Illustrations by
Michael Avery

The Book Guild Ltd.
Sussex, England

The Book Guild Ltd.
25 High Street,
Lewes, Sussex

First published 1994
© Alix Hurd 1994

Set in Souvenir Light

Typesetting by Raven Typesetters
Ellesmere Port, South Wirral

Printed in Great Britain by
Antony Rowe Ltd.
Chippenham, Wiltshire.

A catalogue record for this book is
available from the British Library

ISBN 0 86332 924 1

To
Lesley Ann Jones,
my granddaughter

CONTENTS

CONTENTS

1

The Cyclone

Nineteen forty-five became known as the year of the storm on Labelle Island. The notorious storm was sighted over the Indian Ocean on 15th December at 6 a.m. and warnings were at once broadcast at regular intervals on the wireless:

> 'There is a deep depression gathering force at sea coming towards the south west part of the island at about 10 miles an hour. The tropical storm is expected to hit the island tomorrow at about midday with gale force winds of 80 miles an hour. We will keep you informed of the storm's progress every half hour during the day. Take care and good luck!'

The inhabitants of the island stopped whatever they were doing and made what preparations they could to meet the threatening tempest.

On the De Vere estate, Mrs De Vere, in the main house, put her emergency plans into action. She was ready to shelter any of her tenants or workers who

9

mistrusted the strength of their cottages. Her daughters, Charlotte and Beatrice, were already in the school
building with blankets and food for any other refugees
from the storm.

Mrs De Vere's daughter-in-law and granddaughters
Victoria, aged twelve and Rosie, a year younger,
occupied a large bungalow which was separated from
the main house by a tennis court and the servants'
quarters. The two girls were following their maids, Flo
and Milly, around the house making sure that the
shutters were well fastened and that everywhere was
wind and watertight. Tessa, the cook, was cooking
enough food to last during a long siege. The family was
now prepared and was grouped in the lounge, waiting
and waiting for the arrival of the heralded hurricane.

Sure enough, at noon the next day, there was an
increasing gathering of gloom and the light was
blocked off by huge black clouds. Then there followed
angry rumbles of thunder and at the same time
lightning flashes which fireworked across the sky. The
wind came howling and screeching and – boom – the
heavens exploded and torrential rain poured down.

Strangely enough, Victoria welcomed the feeling of
excitement and fear that came with the advent of an
imminent cyclone. She could recall vaguely a storm
which had come towards the southern part of the
island five years before. That storm had veered off the
island and chosen another target in the ocean just
before reaching its peak. But it had been exciting to
feel the power of the storm whilst being safe in the
house with her family. She was also afraid because
there was always the possibility of disaster. She could
imagine part of the house being badly damaged; who
could tell what evil forces would be unleashed?

The gusting and whistling outside became louder

and Rosie started to cry as the shutters rattled violently.

'Come on, girls,' said their mother, 'let's have a game of cards. Don't worry, Rosie, we are as secure as we can be here.'

'I wish we were in Gran's house,' sobbed Rosie, 'I'd feel safer there!'

'Your Gran may have to shelter many tenants as it is,' replied their mother.

They shuffled the cards and started to play rummy but they could not concentrate, not only because of the din outside but also because of the uncertain flickering electric light. Their mother went to the piano instead. 'Shall we sing all the songs we know, all our favourites and I'll teach you some new ones?' She thumped the piano resoundingly. 'Let's start with the Christmas carols, Christmas is not far off. How about *Silent Night?*'

They were not amused.

A cyclone always struck the island when the summer had been too long and too hot. It was quite capable of bringing down electric and telephone poles, trees and even the shacks in which so many people lived. Vans and cars which had not been parked with care in sheltered places could be overturned and any small boats left at sea ended up on the rocks, smashed into fragments.

All this reduced the island to a state of chaos for several days.

Victoria remembered cousin Andy who, during a bad storm, had gone outside the house to seal up a door of his shed when a sheet of corrugated iron from a nearby roof came flying through the air and smashed into his back. He was lucky to survive but the injuries he sustained left him a cripple. Vicky felt glad she was home and safe.

11

It was now eight o'clock and they could no longer pick up the broadcasts. The radio was dead.

The maids brought in bowls of steaming rice, stir-fried vegetables and slices of grilled fish and meat. The family was surprised to find that they were hungry.

'There won't be any fruits left on the trees after this,' their mother told them, 'so you'd better appreciate these lychees and mangoes Tessa collected and stored for us.'

After the meal the girls helped to carry mattresses and blankets to the lounge, the very middle of the house and the safest place in which to sleep. They had just finished when the electric power failed completely and they went to bed by candlelight.

They listened as the house creaked and groaned; it complained bitterly at being battered and whipped but it stood firm.

Half a mile away on the estate, Widow Benoit and her two sons had only moved into Bramble Cottage the previous day. The cottage, with its corrugated iron roof, was not proving as strong. Mrs Benoit and the two boys, Arthur and Ramon, were huddled together listening to the wind as its mocking and hooting increased.

'Look Mum, the wind is trying to lift the roof there in the corner,' yelled 12-year-old Ramon.

'Yes, it's getting inside, I can feel it, what can we do?' she cried distraughtly.

Suddenly the wind gusted and rose with a jeering howl.

'Look what I can do!' it taunted as part of the roof was forced up, letting the wind whirl and twirl inside.

'Quick!' Arthur shouted. 'Let's get under the dining table, pack chairs and cushions round it, Ramon, take the small tables and put anything else you can find around the sides for protection.'

They worked madly, fetching and carrying what they could handle.

'We're lucky the roof has not gone yet, but one of the sheets was lifted for sure.' Ramon was trying to be as brave as his teenage brother.

They barricaded the dining room table by interlocking chairs around it. They put blankets over it to absorb the shock of anything falling on top. Then they scrambled inside and laid down, petrified, waiting for the worst to happen.

The wind roared with a new onslaught of scorn and the rain pounded the cottage. Water started running down the inside of the wall and they felt the wind snaking in to get at them through the gap it had made in the roof.

The cottage shifted perceptibly. The noise of the wind reached an even higher pitch, as though wild Indians were riding round and round the cottage, shrieking and shouting, ready to attack.

Suddenly, with a whoosh, most of the roof flew away and they heard a splintering sound as some of the supporting beams came down into the room. Elated with what it had done, the wind faded noticeably and appeared to take a rest. Mrs Benoit was the first to speak.

'There's a lull in the storm . . . I think I've hurt my foot . . . are you all right, lads?'

'Yes, we're OK,' replied Arthur. 'We've got to make it to somewhere safer. Unless we are lucky, we'll be in more trouble here.'

He squeezed out through their barricade and got rid of some of the debris which had fallen on and around them. His mother's foot had been caught by a falling rafter which had crashed through their flimsy defences round the table.

'Right!' Arthur ordered. 'Let's make a dash for that bungalow on the estate, it's nearer than the big house. Mum, you'll have to lean on us. We must go now just as we are.'

The Benoits abandoned the cottage whilst the tempest slumbered for a while.

Deep in the night Victoria was woken up by an unnatural peace, a kind of silence, as if the whole of nature outside was waiting. As consciousness returned fully, she realised that they were experiencing the eye of the storm, the time when nature stops; it listens and braces itself before the second phase of the storm. In this calmness and quiet she heard a knocking, followed by a strange female voice crying for help. Was she dreaming? No, there it was again. She was wide awake now.

'Mother, Rosie, wake up, I can hear someone knocking at the front door.'

'Are you sure it's not the wind, dear?' asked her mother sleepily. Then she also listened and heard the voice.

'Come on children, we'll all go to the door and see who it is.'

On the doorstep stood the ghostly figure of a tall, thin woman and, supporting her, two bedraggled boys in soaking wet shorts and singlets.

'Please,' Mrs Benoit started as she came stumbling in and nearly fainted.

'Come in at once, shut the door girls, now what's happened?'

Mrs De Vere pulled them inside the house.

'Children take the torch, go and get the maids and

tell Flo that the lady will need first aid.'

She helped Mrs Benoit through the house to one of the mattresses and made her lie down. The girls returned with Flo who knelt down to examine Mrs Benoit's leg.

'Does this hurt? Or that?' Flo asked. After a few minutes she pronounced, 'It doesn't seem serious, nothing broken, the ankle is badly bruised and perhaps twisted. I'll put a bandage on it and the lady will be more comfortable.'

Milly came forward. 'Would you Mrs . . . like a drop of rum?' she enquired.

'I am Mrs Benoit, the new tenant in Bramble Cottage. Yes, please.'

Some colour returned to her cheeks after she sipped the rum. Rosie had been looking at the boys with curiosity. At last she whispered to them. 'Come over here,' and she led them, followed by Victoria, to the dining area. 'We don't know you? Where have you come from?'

'My name's Arthur and this is my brother, Ramon. We only moved into Bramble Cottage yesterday and we hadn't even finished unpacking when, whack, the cyclone arrived.'

'How terrible for you!' Rosie said with concern.

'We've had rotten luck,' Ramon put in. 'The roof was ripped off by the wind and we had to hide under the table in the living room.'

'Perhaps, then, it was a good thing you hadn't finished unpacking,' said Vicky sensibly.

'We travelled from Limoux the day before yesterday and we heard then that the cyclone might avoid the island and hit Flat Island instead; they always seem to get it wrong.'

He felt like blaming somebody for their misfortune.

17

'You will be all right here, this house is very solid,' Vicky reassured them. 'Now that there are four of us we could even play some games like cards, dominoes or Monopoly . . .'

At this moment, for the first time in his life, Arthur looked and noticed a girl properly. In the glow of the candlelight he saw a girl nearly as tall as himself. She was slim and had large eyes in an attractive face on a long aristocratic neck. Both she and her sister had black curls, in total contrast to his and Ramon's straight fair hair. In spite of himself, his eyes went down to her budding breasts and he hoped at once that it was too dark for the girls to see him blush.

'My name is Victoria but everyone calls me Vicky and Rose is my little sister,' Vicky smiled.

'Called Rosie,' Rosie added, 'and not so little either.'

Cook, having been woken up by the ongoing activity, brought them some hot chocolate. She was keeping a charcoal burner lit although she was aware of the danger of possible sparks and fire in a wooden dwelling. On returning to the kitchen with the empty mugs, she saw that a small window had been forced open by the renewed intensity of the second phase of the storm. She screamed for help. As the wind and rain rushed in, her candle went out and saucepans and crockery were all blown off the shelves. She quickly put her back against the window and shouted until the children and the maids heard her and dashed in.

'What's wrong?' Vicky cried.

'Help me with the window,' shouted Tessa.

'Try to shut it while I put out the burner completely, it's too dangerous to leave it alight.'

'The wind has undone and broken the shutter outside,' Arthur said. 'We can repair the shutter. Do you have any wood and nails?'

18

'I'll get the torch,' Ramon said, 'so we can see what we are doing.'

Flo and Milly found the wood and, with Arthur and Ramon, went outside, in spite of the risk, to nail slats across the shutter and make it secure. They got totally soaked, but returned unharmed inside.

It was not until four o'clock in the morning that everyone in the bungalow was able to fall asleep. The girls let the Benoits have their mattresses and fetched others from the guest room for themselves to rest for the remaining hours.

Night merged into day and still the storm raged outside. During the next day Mrs De Vere and the maids fussed over Mrs Benoit and tried to pass the rest of the time as normally as possible. The two girls also went out of their way to make the boys feel at home. They taught them to play canasta. When they tired of that they played Monopoly which started before lunch and went on until they were hungry again. Rosie got bored and suggested that they play snakes and ladders after dinner. When they got fed up with the game Rosie went to bed early leaving Ramon to play patience and the other two to talk together.

'Do you like reading, Arthur?' Vicky wanted to know.

'It's one of my favourite hobbies,' he answered.

'That's good, I'll show you my books and if you like you can choose one to read now and one to take home to borrow . . .' she invited.

'Thanks, I'd like that,' he smiled. 'Do you have any boys' books?'

'Wait a minute, I'll go and fetch some books and you can see.'

He did not tell her that he only had a couple of books of his own. He normally borrowed the books he

19

needed from the library. She came back with an armful of books and he chose her copy of *Treasure Island* which he would enjoy reading again. But he did not start to read at once because he wanted to talk to Victoria.

I've never met a girl like her before, he was telling himself, she is so friendly and she talks sensibly, like a boy.

He had no sisters and the few girls he had met until now were either shy or burst out into giggles for no reason at all. It was so irritating!

They talked and shared jokes, laughing happily and they hardly noticed the continuing storm.

Outside the wind swirled high, looking for branches, leaves and roofs to fling away; then it swirled low searching for roots to unearth or trees to uproot. The cyclone lasted two days and nights after which the wind became exhausted, it was totally spent and slowly petered out.

The following morning all was calm. Mrs Benoit and her sons wanted to return to Bramble Cottage and face the worst.

'Don't worry, Mrs Benoit,' said Mrs De Vere, 'my mother-in-law will send workers to do the necessary repairs as soon as she can. There is not much wrong here, so I can come and help you too; send one of the boys if you need me.'

As the Benoits were leaving, the children said good-bye to each other.

'Can we stay friends?' Rosie wanted to know.

'I'm not sure, we prefer to play with boys,' Ramon blurted out.

Arthur was shy but said, 'Ramon, how rude!'

'Sorry!' Ramon conceded. 'Anyway, thank you very much for having us.'

'We *will* stay friends,' Victoria promised determin-
edly.

She sensed in her heart that their meeting on that
unforgettable night, under such extraordinary circum-
stances, would have a profound effect on their lives.

2

De Vere Domaine

Victoria went outdoors and took a deep breath. After a cyclone the air was so fresh and pure, not an atom of dust and dirt was left; all had been swept away over the ocean.

The pale, blushing sun was spreading its soft light over the ravaged landscape. It appeared to be apologising for the bad manners of its friends, the wind and rain. 'At times my friends do not know how to behave; they go berserk and at present they are ashamed and in hiding. But I'm here now to bring some peace, warmth and order back into the world.' The sun glowed harder.

Victoria looked at the maids bustling and several workers sweeping, repairing and salvaging. A boy came towards her.

'Your Gran, Mrs De Vere, wants to know how things are here and if you need anything?' he asked.

'Yes, tell her that we survived and that we are well but we had to shelter Mrs Benoit and she needed first aid.'

'Mum,' Vicky shouted. 'I'm going to Gran's to tell her everything.'

She made her way cautiously to the main house, avoiding the wreckage. The tennis court was not damaged, but the wire netting enclosure had caught masses of flying litter. She could not help getting wet feet because there were still rivulets of water everywhere. All the drains and ditches had been blocked by falling leaves and sticks.

As she approached the main house she felt a pang of sadness for her grandmother. Gran took such pride and joy in her garden and spent hours working in it herself. It was a formal garden, based on a French design. There were enormous flower beds, boxed in by privet hedges to form mini gardens. She had a rose garden, a garden of cana lilies, one of wild flowers and one of arums grown specially for church decoration. The lawns themselves went down to a pool covered with water lilies. Once a year she opened the garden to the public and the proceeds went to charity. Now all the bushes and the plants had been despoiled and petals of all colours festooned the lawn and hedges, reminiscent of confetti after a wedding.

The house itself stood majestically at the end of a circular drive. It had been planned in the style of a Normandy chateau and it was made of stone. The roof was covered with wooden tiles to simulate slate and many of these were now missing. The house would be forbidding had it not been usually covered with masses of creepers such as red, orange and mauve bougainvilleas, wisteria and honeysuckle, but these were now lying in heaps at the foot of the walls like discarded clothing, but hopefully not uprooted. Most of the flame trees lining the drive were also bare of their leaves and flowers.

Mrs De Vere was on the verandah surveying the devastation of the cyclone and organising the cleaning and mopping up operation.

23

'What a mess, Grandma!' Vicky exclaimed as she went up the steps.

'Yes! It was a bad one, but I have seen worse. I heard you managed well but the Benoit woman needed help. I forgot all about her after she moved in. Doctor Dumas will visit her this afternoon and her cottage is being repaired at the moment.'

'Who is she, Grandma? We liked her sons and we became friends,' Vicky stated in her normal, forthright fashion. Her grandmother did not reply straightaway.

'Look at all this, Vicky,' she said at last, making a sweeping gesture, 'we own the fields, the hills and the woods as far as you can see.'

'I know, Gran, but . . .'

Vicky was interrupted. 'Our ancestors built everything you can see on this land. They planted the trees and the fields of sugar cane and they ensured the future for those who followed them. We, you and I, have a responsibility to take up that inheritance in our own interests and in those of all the staff and tenants who depend on us.'

'But what has that to do with the Benoits, Grandma?'

'Mrs Benoit is now one of my tenants. She has been recommended by Prior Jules as a good woman in need of work and shelter. I have accepted her to help with the nursery school on the estate and in return she can stay at Bramble Cottage. I wanted simply to remind you of your responsibilities and that you must be careful with whom you make friends if you have the interests of the family and the estate at heart.'

Vicky followed her grandmother inside the house, which was shared with her aunts, Beatrice and Charlotte, and Uncle Roland, all three unmarried. Roland now ran the sugar estate since Vicky's own father, the eldest child, had died. He had been learning to fly and was practising on his own when he lost control, crashed and was killed in front of her mother.

Vicky was greeted by her aunts and again mentioned the Benoits to them. 'She will help me teach the young ones on the estate,' said Aunt Bee. 'She is keen to live near the Monastery where her sons are going to be educated.'

Snatches of conversation which Vicky had heard from the adults recently and ignored came back to her: 'poor whites . . . good church-goer . . . as a Christian duty . . .' and so on.

'Come on, Vicky, sit down and tell us what happened at the bungalow during the cyclone.'

She started to tell them what they had done during the storm. After she had mentioned the boys for the umpteenth time, her grandmother stopped her and with her 'sermon voice' said: 'Victoria, you and Rosie know full well that you are allowed to play with any of the children on the estate. Roland and myself ensure that we employ well-behaved people who work hard and who know their place.'

That's the trouble, thought Victoria, you can't be really friendly with them, they are so servile, but she did not say it aloud.

Her grandmother went on. 'Your father is unfortunately not here to keep an eye on you. Within the estate you can be friendly in a polite way with the new boys; you can even share your books and play tennis with them, but outside the estate you are not to mention them and you must ignore the boys if you meet them and do not talk about them to schoolfriends . . . socially the Benoits are not acceptable in the circle in which we live, is that understood?'

Victoria understood very well that she was being

asked to be two-faced, which was not in her nature. She did not argue with her grandmother but she could not help questioning in her mind why they could go out of their way to be kind to the poor but they could not show others that they were friendly with them. But such instructions had never been difficult to follow because she and Rosie both lived two completely separate lives anyway. The one outside the estate consisted of school, of dancing, singing, art and piano lessons; the one on the estate meant being free as the air, free to play, to run, to climb trees, to swim in the pools of the river which skirted the estate, to ride horses, to have pets, all whilst surrounded by a loving family and their loyal employees.

Once the havoc of the storm was cleaned up, life on the estate returned to this norm for the girls with the addition of the new friendship with the boys. On the Saturday after the storm the girls rode their horses to Bramble Cottage and found them working in the garrrden.

'Hello, you two, would you like to jump on? We want to show you some of our favourite places on the hills and in the woods. We'd like to have a swim too, it's still humid, so the water is nice. Ask your Mum if you can come.' Victoria was making sure that they knew by her tone of voice she would not accept a 'No!'

'We'll ask Mum if we can finish later,' said Arthur.

They rode through the woods and on around the rows of sugar canes, past the idle sugar cane factory. They went along the river, looking for their favourite pool. Volcanic action in the past had resulted in a series of pools looking from above like an extended string of pearls. After an hour of such exploration, Arthur remarked. 'We are lucky to have come to Domaine De Vere, it's such an interesting place, it's got everything.'

27

'Yes, I agree,' said Ramon, being polite.

'Ah, here's the pool!' the girls shouted.

They dismounted, tethered the horses, changed behind some bushes and swam in the fresh water. The river had also been flushed clean by the torrential rains and now the pool was crystal-clear.

'Look,' explained Rosie. 'Hold this liane . . . swing like this and when you reach the middle you let go and oh . . . it's lovely!'

Some time later, as they were lying on the bank drying, Arthur sat up. 'What's that noise?' he asked.

'It's coming from behind that rock, over there,' pointed Vicky.

The four got up and ran along the bank down the river. The whining noise was clearly coming from a bag which had become snagged on an overhanging branch and was half way out of the water. Arthur waded in and pulled the sack off the branch. They all heard the whimpering again as Arthur frantically tried to undo or snap the string around the bag. Finally he managed to untie it.

'Oh!' cried the children,' who can do such a cruel thing?'

To their horror they saw three puppies in the sack. They had obviously been thrown into the river to drown. Two had already drowned but the third was still alive and whining. All they could make out was a ball of saturated black fur and a round head. Two dark eyes looked at them fearfully and the bright pink mouth opened wide as it wailed again. Victoria pulled it out and stroked it as the others crowded round.

'Let's go back home quickly,' cried Victoria. 'We must, we must save the little pup.'

28

3

Moses

Moses, as they called him from his watery beginnings, loved his four saviours. He also loved Tessa who fed him so carefully on the first and subsequent days. He would come bounding in whenever she called him or rattled his bowl wherever he was and his appetite was limitless; he wolfed down everything put before him. At first Mrs De Vere looked at the pup with pity and sorrow but soon she had to like him for being so friendly and for showing his appreciation, he was so glad to be alive when his brothers had drowned. He grew fast and, as Victoria remarked, was beginning to look like a retriever.

Moses' trust in human nature was astonishing considering his early experience. He liked and greeted every person who came to the estate as a friend, wagging his tail and whipping their legs in delight. He was just as welcoming with other dogs, even if sometimes a larger dog came snarling at him with bared teeth. He would retreat, find one of the four or Tessa to complain and to sulk but he did not learn, he still cared for everybody.

29

The friends tried to teach him tricks and to train him to be a 'proper' dog but their efforts were largely unsuccessful. He was too affectionate and full of fun to take training seriously. Take the time when they played hide and seek and Moses was 'on'. Before the count of ten was up and they had time to hide, he had found each one of them in a flash. They fell about laughing and could not stop.

'OK, Moses,' scolded Rosie the next time they played. 'You must lie very still with me so that Ramon cannot find you, do you follow? No yelping, no wag of the tail, clear?'

Moses cocked his head and showed his agreement with a grin. He laid down and put his head on his front paws, as if asleep. But then, just as Ramon was approaching their spot, Moses yawned the loudest imaginable yawn and gave the game away. Rosie was too amused to be cross.

Moses enjoyed chasing cats and rabbits and he was excellent at retrieving sticks and balls and he sometimes even caught young birds.

'I don't kill them, I just play,' he wanted them to know as he deposited the little creatures at their feet. They reprimanded him but he did not learn.

Amazingly enough, Moses was not afraid of water. When the children swam he joined them and tried to retrieve them so that they had to keep a ball to throw for him to fetch instead. He even accepted with good grace being washed clean occasionally.

Moses was seven months old when he disappeared. The girls returned from school and he was not there to greet them.

'Have you seen Moses, Tessa?' they asked. 'Has Uncle Roland taken him somewhere?'

They went to look at his bowl which was still full of

food. They became worried and called 'Moses! Moses!' but no sloppy dog came rushing to them.

Arthur and Ramon arrived to join in the daily ritual of homework. They too were concerned to find that Moses was missing.

'No-one would want to steal him, would they?' Rosie asked.

Vicky took command. 'Look! We know he does not like to go very far from the villa. We'll search for him on foot. Rosie to the north, Arthur east by the river, me south and Ramon west. We'll whistle to each other as we go and whistle several times in succession if we find him. Rosie can take the guide whistle because she still can't whistle properly. Tessa, tell Mum and Aunt Bee that we'll be back before it gets dark.' Vicky could be very bossy.

They searched and called and still heard no answering bark. Their whistling was becoming fainter and fainter. After a whole hour they were downhearted and dejected when they heard the repeated whistle signal coming from Arthur's south-eastern section. Three pairs of feet ran as fast as they could to where Arthur was trying to revive a half-dead Moses.

'Is he all right? Where was he?' They asked eagerly.

'It's a miracle,' Arthur explained. 'I reached the river and I knew that Moses would not have crossed over. Everything was so calm, so quiet and I was scanning the undergrowth there when I saw the very tip of his tail, just one little bit showing. I ran up and scooped off a mound of leaves which had only recently been dislodged and there was the backside of Moses. The idiotic dog had most of himself stuck in this hole and his head got trapped by roots. Come and see.'

They walked to the hole to examine it. Arthur continued, 'I had to cut these to release him. I bet he saw something go down the hole. In his excitement, he followed so fast he got caught by the roots which acted like a noose. He tried to back out, which made the noose tighter. He kicked and dislodged the wet earth and leaves which fell on him and buried him. He was practically asphyxiated.'

Victoria cuddled the dog. 'Come here, you foolish dog, and say thank you to Arthur for saving you. If you were a cat, Moses, I'd say that you've had two of your nine lives.'

She stroked the slobbering, soft-hearted puppy they loved and, relieved, they made their way back to homework and tea.

4

School

During the year that followed the storm the children's life took on a certain pattern. They went to school during the day. Back home the four did their homework together at the long table in the protected part of the verandah, supervised by one of the aunts.

At weekends, they played together and looked for adventures. Some weekends they had to go different ways. The girls entertained other friends or relatives or they themselves were invited elsewhere. The boys' lives mostly revolved round the estate, the school and the girls.

Victoria and Rosie attended a private school for girls in town. They were proud to be the first girls in their family to go to school instead of being educated at home haphazardly by a governess or tutor. Their grandmother was not so sure it was a good idea but admitted, 'We can't teach them at home now that they need laboratories for science; we can't have labs on the estate.'

The school used to be a grand colonial house with vast lawns which were now the playing fields. If you asked the girls what their school was like, they would have answered, 'All right!' No more, no less. School was not exciting; it was a 'crammer' which means a place where pupils are trained solely to pass their final examinations in certain subjects, on which they have little choice. To be accepted by the school all the pupils had to pass an entrance test. Once in, they had to keep up with each other. If anyone, through illness perhaps, fell behind, they were given extra tuition to catch up. Every girl was expected to behave well all the time. No chatting in class was allowed, no answering back to teachers. Two warnings were given to anyone who broke the rules; then the parents were called in and asked to find another school for their daughter.

Both Victoria and Rosie were good pupils. No-one at home pushed them hard but they did enough to enjoy their studies, although they did find some subjects boring such as Latin, handwriting and algebra. On the other hand they paid for art, dancing and piano lessons which were extra subjects and they both enjoyed games and sports. They liked to compete and would willingly practise harder to win prizes and pass tests to get certificates.

Victoria liked her main teacher who also taught French. She was young and elegant and dressed like a Parisienne. In contrast Rosie's teacher, Mrs Simonet, was the oldest teacher in the school, dowdy, and about to retire.

Unaccountably, Rosie was not feeling well at the beginning of the summer term. She felt sick in the mornings and was reluctant to go to school. Her mother noticed, however, that she recovered miraculously during the day.

'Shall I send for Dr Dumas, Rosie?'

'Oh no, Mummy, the tummy ache is gone now.'

35

'I thought you had a headache?'

'It was more like an earache.'

After a couple of days Mrs De Vere asked Vicky whether anything had happened at school to upset her sister.

'Oh yes, I forgot to tell you, old Mrs Simonet is sick and the Head had to get a replacement teacher quickly, a Miss Drout. She is young like Mademoiselle, but she is strict and her class hates her.'

'I see, thank you Vicky, I'd better have a word with Rosie: call her for me.'

Rosie advanced sheepishly.

'I am sad to hear,' began her mother, 'that Mrs Simonet is not well, but that is not a reason for missing school, Rosie. You must be more grown up and learn what it is that the new teacher wants of her class.'

'She is horrible, Mummy, we don't like her,' she murmured.

'She is new, Rosie, perhaps she is finding it difficult to adapt to her class, you must give her a chance and do your best and give a good example to the rest of the class.'

'I'll try, but I wish Mrs Simonet would come back soon, we do miss her.'

'No-one likes changes, Rosie, promise me that you will try harder.'

'Yes, Mummy, I'll try.'

A few days later, during homework, Ramon suddenly shouted, 'Miss Bee, look at Rosie's hand, look at her hands!'

Rosie started to cry and tried to hide her hands behind her back.

'Show me, Rosie,' asked her aunt and her mother who had been alerted by the noise.

Two angry red weals were embossed on both her

hands. They gulped in dismay.

'She said it was my fault,' cried Rosie. 'I kept playing the wrong notes but I could not help it, she frightens me.'

Then it all came pouring out of her. How Miss Drout hated her and the twins from the next estate; she called them slave owners or little snobs.

'We can't do anything right but I don't know what I am doing wrong.' Big sobs racked her.

Mrs De Vere was on the phone at once to Grandmother and then to the twins' parents to discuss this unprecedented development at the girls' school.

The next day the girls went to school as usual. At 11 a.m. Gran De Vere, Mrs De Vere and Uncle Roland arrived to keep the appointment they had made to see the headmistress. The Head listened to them before sending for Miss Drout and for Rosie. The child, trembling, showed her hands still red and scarred.

'She asked for it,' started Miss Drout. 'She deliberately played the wrong notes. The child needs discipline.'

'I don't, I don't!' cried Rosie.

'That will do Rosie,' said the Head kindly. 'Go and wash your face in the cloakroom before going back to your class.'

'How dare you?' exclaimed Uncle Roland to Miss Drout. 'How dare you cane Rosie? If you were a man . . . I have a good mind to report you to Inspector Dunville for assault.'

'There is no need,' interrupted the Head. 'Miss Drout is only with us temporarily. She won't . . .'

'No, I won't stay,' yelled Miss Drout. 'I have no desire to stay and teach stuck-up brainless girls who need better discipline.' She ran out of the room.

On the way back to the estate Gran De Vere mused.

37

'Do you think Miss Drout is descended from a slave?'

'Even if she is, she can't take it out on a girl like Rosie. How can you be a teacher if you are prejudiced against some pupils?' Uncle Roland asked.

After the incident, when Mrs Simonet returned she agreed to stay at school after her retirement whilst a more suitable replacement was found for her.

The boys' school was totally different. They went to the Monastery School on the edge of town. The Monastery stood in a large field surrounded by high walls like a Middle Ages castle and the school was situated near the main entrance. The monks ran a good school and parents willingly paid for their boys to be educated there. It was more interesting than the girls' school because it catered not only for boys who learnt academic subjects but for those boys who wanted a technical education. However, in common with the girls' school, all the pupils had to pass an entrance test. They had to be clever and wish to learn and they had to behave themselves or else!

Victoria knew that Mrs Benoit could not afford to pay for Arthur's and Ramon's schooling. Arthur explained the mystery by volunteering the information that his father had been the chief printer at the monks' other monastery. One day during work, he was disturbed and his hand caught in some machinery and was crushed. It became infected and poisoned his blood and he eventually died. Following his death the monks felt a certain responsibility; they gave the boys free schooling and granted their mother a small pension. Despite the accident which killed his father, Arthur was determined to become a printer too. He wanted to be in charge of the pressroom and perhaps one day to work on a newspaper; and he loved the smell of printing. Because of this fondness, he was always reading and writing and was considered a promising student. Monk René was even hoping that Arthur might feel inspired to become a monk one day. Too few young men were willing to become monks these days and the old monks were getting older and older and were not being replaced.

The leaflets and books which were printed in the Monastery were carried from the pressroom to the main building and to the school and shop in an old van. Arthur was working with Monk René who these days was always so tired he had to have longer and longer rest periods.

'Thank goodness that's the last load,' said the monk. 'I don't know how I would manage without your strong arms, Arthur. Give me a glass of water so I can recover. I don't even have the strength to drive today. You're thirteen, aren't you? Learn to drive Arthur, it would be a great help.'

An idea flashed into Arthur's mind. 'I think I might be able to learn,' he replied.

The monks were practically self-sufficient. They were experts at raising money for their charitable projects. One of their favourites was to give scholarships to boys who were keen to learn. Some of these old pupils whom they had helped had become doctors, lawyers and even a bishop. Others became good carpenters or printers or gardeners which was equally gratifying.

On their two-day summer fête in the Monastery grounds, the monks sold what they, their pupils and others from the wider community had made or produced. On the first day was the fair itself and on the second the prizegiving and sports day. Many people came on the first day as helpers and then as buyers. The fête in the year after the storm was particularly well supported. There were tents everywhere and, with the Monastery walls in the background, the fête quite resembled Camelot. Vicky, who had arrived with Rosie on the first day to take part in the gymkhana, exclaimed, 'I can just imagine knights in shining armour coming to take part in jousting tournaments with banners flying, can't you?'

'And us the ladies with pointed hats?' asked Rosie.

They laughed and made their way to the handicrafts stall. Vicky collected rag dolls of all sizes and always bought one or two here. Rosie liked anything made of patchwork. On the white elephant stall they both looked for tiny, coloured glass oil lamps; they had a collection of nineteen which they took pride in lighting up for a party. In their bags went jars of jam and there was enough room left for some old and new books. Arthur and Ramon helped to run the bookstall.

'How are you doing?' Vicky asked the boys.

'Better than last year already, we are told.'

'Any books you can recommend for us to buy?'

'Yes, I would not mind having these myself,' Arthur told Vicky.

Both girls bought two books each.

'We are going off now to have some tea and cakes, otherwise Tessa won't forgive us. She's made tons of cakes, scones and biscuits for the cakes' stall and an enormous 'Guess the weight' cake.'

'What's the weight then? Tell us,' teased Ramon.

'I want to try some of the amusements before I go to the gymkhana,' Vicky said.

'I'll come and watch you ride,' Arthur called after them. 'There is something I want to tell you,' he whispered as he caught up with her, 'and something I want to ask you.'

'OK, see you later!' she nodded before running away.

Vicky ate a piece of cherry cake whilst Rosie chose a plain sponge slice. They were not hungry but eager to try the coconut shy and the bobbing apples. They failed at both. There was a crowd at one stall and, on inspection, they saw that the boys were enjoying throwing wet sponges at Monk René. The girls did not fancy doing that but would have tried the rifle shooting run by Uncle Roland or the archery but it was time for the gymkhana events.

As she neared the field Vicky greeted one of her neighbours from the next estate, who was riding a beautiful chestnut mare.

'Suzanne, what a beauty, I've never seen her before, is she yours?'

'Yes, I've had her a month, she was a present. I've been taking professional dressage lessons from Mr Tulie. He says we are good enough to win.'

'We ride for fun really but Arthur does help me to practise,' Vicky said as Arthur turned up to watch. Suzanne looked at him disdainfully and then asked, 'Is he your groom?'

'No, I'm her friend,' Arthur replied as he led Vicky and her horse away.

In spite of Mr Tulie's lessons, Suzanne and her horse did not win, nor did Vicky. Rosie, on the other hand, had a clear round and came first in her event.

The next day the girls could not attend the prize-giving and sports day because they had been invited to a friend's birthday party. But they were extremely pleased when they heard that Arthur had won the literature prize in his year and Ramon the maths one and also the long jump in the sports. They brought their trophies to show the girls that evening.

Vicky then reminded Arthur, 'You had something to tell me and something to ask me, Arthur, what is it?'

'Let's take Moses for a walk and I'll tell you . . . Well, the most extraordinary thing happened when Monk René and I were carrying the books to the fête. First thing in the morning we heard someone on the other side of the wall, singing, laughing in a stupid way and, believe me, even swearing.

' "Oh Lord forgive us our sins," prayed Monk René.

'We dashed into the next courtyard and there was Monk Sam, drunk as you please with a bottle of rum in his hand, making all this noise. He was completely drunk, Vicky.'

' "Help me Arthur," asked Monk René and between us we took him back to his cell, still singing and swaying. Another monk came to help and then he went to fetch Prior Jules.

' "Leave this to me," said Prior Jules and just as Monk René and I were leaving he looked at me and added, "Be discreet, young man."

'Monk René was ashamed. "I'm sorry you've had to witness this, Arthur, Brother Sam is our best distiller, the sale of rum brings us a lot of money which we use for charity, as you know . . ."

'I tell you, Vicky, it was the biggest shock of my life, I regarded these monks as something like angels and now I find that they can behave the same as any other man. Please don't tell anybody else, but I had to tell someone . . .'

'I won't tell,' she promised, 'and I am as shocked as you are.'

They walked in silence for a while before Vicky put the next question.

'What were you going to ask me?'

'Oh yes, I nearly forgot . . . Can you teach me to

42

drive, Vicky? You once told me that Fred taught you to drive when you were ten but I don't believe he would teach me would he?' He went on. 'I tell you why. Monk René and I take all the printed stuff in the van from one building to another and he is getting too old to drive or to teach me for that matter. He told me to learn and I think that I'll stand a better chance of winning the printing apprenticeship if I do.'

'Yes, I am sure I could teach you. Fred is a pal. I have borrowed the wagon from him before. He was so pleased I wanted to learn to drive, but I'm not sure he would be prepared to teach you. Did you know he and Flo are getting married? I'll borrow the station wagon and we'll go to the south of the estate; there are fewer people there. That's where I learnt. Let's do it this weekend. What about Saturday at 4 p.m.? I'll pick you up near Bramble Cottage. I say, Arthur, when you learn to drive, you will be able to take your test before me when you are fifteen; it's not fair!' Vicky joked.

'What if I can't learn?'

'Of course you will! You do realise that we can't drive out of the estate?' she said.

'Yes, or outside the Monastery walls,' Arthur added. 'In return I know what I shall do for you Vicky.'

'There is no need for you to repay me, Arthur, we are friends that's enough.'

'Yes, but I would like to build you the best tree house you have ever seen in your life.'

'Wonderful! What a great idea! Where? When? It's a deal! Hurrah!' And she skipped away laughing.

5

The Lesson

Vicky borrowed the station wagon from Fred, their driver. She knew that he would refuse to lend it if she mentioned Arthur.

'I want to do some practising on my own,' she lied.

'You forgetting how to drive, Miss Vicky? I trust you to bring it back in one piece now.'

'I promise I won't let you down, Fred.'

She drove cautiously and took the long way round to the wood near Bramble Cottage where Arthur was waiting for her. They drove off together down to the old sugar road. Arthur confessed that he was quite nervous.

'I already know what to do in theory, Vicky. Now let me see if I can do it in practice.'

'Let me show you how this car works,' she explained. 'You have to be very careful with the clutch.'

After a few minutes Arthur took over. 'Right, I press down the clutch, put it in first gear and release the clutch slowly,' he recited.

The wagon started to jump like a kangaroo and Vicky laughed so much that she cried.

'Press the clutch down and start again,' she said.

Arthur was disheartened by his apparent failure but he tried again and soon he was confident enough to drive round in first gear.

'It's difficult to steer and drive at the same time,' he said.

Then, feeling exhilarated by the power and with his pulse racing, he accelerated too much and the car rattled and shook.

'Change into second gear, Arthur,' Vicky told him. He tried again and the wagon shot forward as he changed too quickly. He had to brake but he applied the brakes too hard and stalled the engine.

'This is proving harder than I expected,' he admitted.

After an hour Arthur managed to get into all the gears and to steer the wagon at the same time but he felt completely exhausted and was covered with perspiration.

'Let me take over,' Vicky said. 'That's enough for one day. Another two or three lessons and you'll be an expert,' she reassured him.

She felt genuinely pleased with him and with herself.

'Thank you, teacher,' he said.

'In the hols I'll show you how to do some maintenance on the engine and how to change the wheels.'

'That'll be great Vicky. Now to change the subject completely, tell me where you want the tree house to be.'

'On the way back I'll stop and show you. We must be quick or Fred will start to worry.'

Fortunately it did not take her long to park the car in the sugar road and walk to the middle of the wood to find the tree they wanted. Vicky was then able to return the car to Fred.

'When is the wedding, Fred?' she asked.

'This year, Miss Vicky, in September when it's not too hot.'

'That's nice, here is something towards the wedding, Fred.' She gave him some money.

'Thanks, Miss Vee, every little bit helps. Flo and I are sure saving hard. Did you get some good practice? I'm glad the wagon's OK, I only serviced it yesterday.'

The next time Victoria talked to Uncle Roland she mentioned casually, 'Arthur is keen to get the printing scholarship at the Monastery, Uncle, is there any way you can help him? I know our family has influence with the Monastery and you are friendly with Prior Jules.'

'How do you think I can do that, my dear girl? Do you suggest I ask the monks to give him the scholarship and I'll give them ten more bags of sugar? Or shall I blackmail them: unless you give Arthur what he wants, we'll not make any more cakes for the fête and I'll stop our contributions to your funds?'

'Oh Uncle, don't laugh at me,' Victoria pouted. 'I only wanted to help a friend. He is very proud and does not know I am asking you to put in a good word on his behalf. He is working very hard for the exams and hopes he will beat the other candidates.'

'Well, the boy certainly has a good pal in you. He can drive now, I hear, and that should help him to pass his driving test when the time comes, if nothing else.' And then he became serious. 'I hope you are not forgetting what we've told you. You mustn't become too close to these boys. Remember your place on the estate . . . we have plans for you.'

Vicky hardly heeded the now familiar lecture.

As her uncle walked away, Victoria hoped that she had sown a little seed in his mind and that it might grow so that when he met Prior Jules he would remember to mention Arthur's talents. She suddenly stopped dead and asked herself, how does Uncle Roland know I've been teaching Arthur to drive?

6

The Tree House

The tree they had chosen in the centre of the wood was an enormous ebony tree. It forked right in the middle and the two parts forked again exactly as Arthur wanted it to. There were many branches which interlocked with branches of adjacent trees. It was perfect.

'I'll collect some planks, there are plenty left lying around on the estate behind the sheds. I've got nails, and all the necessary tools I can borrow from the Monastery. I'll come back and measure with Ramon during the week and next weekend we can make a start.' Arthur was planning aloud.

'Arthur, listen, I have lots of things we can use once you've put the floor in. There's bags of stuff in Gran's attic. I've seen a rope ladder there which belonged to my dad. Promise you won't buy anything. Let me have a list of what we need, of what you can provide and I can tell you what I can find. Once we've got everything ready I'll borrow the station wagon again to carry the things here.'

The girls had such fun searching in their Gran's loft for the rope ladder and another strong rope, an old

49

red cotton rug, a pair of rather faded blue curtains, a leather pouffe, and a small table which had once been in the nursery. In their attic they found a campbed, two large blankets, some cushions and tuck boxes in which to keep biscuits and cakes and two sleeping bags.

At the weekend, Arthur started work on the tree house. From the safety of the first fork he nailed a few short cross beams to provide a basic platform. Using these he was then able to tie the strong rope on the left branch. At once Ramon hoisted himself up the rope and helped Arthur to fasten the rope ladder on a big branch on the right. The girls tried to climb up the ladder but this proved quite difficult as it swung madly. Eventually Ramon secured the ladder at the bottom to the ground with a stake. At last the girls, like Ramon, mastered the rope and the ladder and they felt a sense of achievement as they reached the safety of the fork. After an hour or so the floor was beginning to take shape. They all jumped up and down on it to make sure it was strong enough to support them. Arthur had taken special care and it passed the test. When they went home that evening, they were happy that they were creating a place of their own from which to see the world. On succeeding weekends they helped Arthur add walls and a makeshift roof of corrugated iron to give their hideaway the feel of a real house.

Once they had finished the building itself, they started to furnish it with the objects they had collected. It took them ages to carry things up the tree only to find that some would not fit or were not suitable. But at last the tree house was finished to their satisfaction, and Vicky tacked the blue curtains at the window.

'It's a smashing house. Thank you, Arthur,' Vicky told him. 'Another thing I like with it is that you can climb one branch higher to a sort of lookout post and

see for miles over Domaine De Vere.'

'What are you going to call the house, Vicky?' Arthur wanted to know.

'What about the Benoit Lodge?' asked Ramon.

'Or De Vere's Haven?' from Rosie.

'I have already decided, if it is all right with Arthur, I'd like to call it simply Tree Tops,' said Vicky.

'Tree Tops it is then,' accepted Arthur.

'Good, let's have a house warming party,' said Vicky full of enthusiasm.

'Do you want to invite other guests?' asked Ramon.

'Oh no, it's private,' said Arthur.

'We've only got biscuits and lemonade, is that enough?' asked Vicky.

'Yes, that will do very nicely indeed,' Ramon was feeling hungry.

Vicky got the paper cups and the lemonade whilst Rosie found the tin of biscuits. 'Cheers!' they toasted each other. 'To our hide-out!'

7

Walking on Fire

It was only because of the tree house that the children were able to witness two happenings within a month. One sunny Sunday afternoon they were lazing about in their new 'home' after having feasted on a full picnic basket provided by Tessa. They were now playing a rather desultory game of dominoes as the warmth of the day and the food made them all drowsy. Moses had refused to be left on guard at the bottom of the tree and instead had to be carried up by Arthur only to fall asleep on the rug. Suddenly, Moses looked up and listened attentively with his head on one side. The four also listened and heard music coming faintly in the distance. Rosie scrambled to their higher lookout post and made out a native procession of local people in the distance on the neighbouring estate. These processions were not allowed on the De Vere estate because the participants sometimes took days off work. Flo, Milly and Tessa were all afraid of them too and warned that those who took part in them were under a spell which children could catch as some sort of disease.

'Let's go and see what they are up to,' said

bold Vicky.

'If we hide carefully and follow from afar no-one will see us.' Arthur said, not the least bit afraid.

'We'll be trespassing, but we won't touch anything,' said Rosie. 'Anyway Suzanne is always inviting us over; who is going to hold Moses?'

'We'll take it in turns,' Vicky said firmly, she was good at taking decisions.

Having noted the path of the procession, it was easy for them to clamber down the tree to follow the sound of the music from a safe range, hiding behind bushes. Ten minutes later they were near enough to see the parade as it moved into a large clearing. Waiting to receive this strange collection of people was a group of women dressed in brightly coloured sarongs. They were tending on the ground a rectangle of burning charcoal.

The musicians went on playing their strange music and those immediately following them were dancing and swaying, apparently in some kind of trance. Behind the dancers were groups of people carrying on their shoulders floats which were covered completely with garlands of flowers.

To the children's astonishment, they saw that some of the dancers, both men, women and youngsters, had metal pins stuck through their cheeks and their tongues and through the skins of their chests and backs. They seemed to be quite unaware of any pain and there was no blood to be seen.

But their surprise was compounded by the next stage in the ceremony. The procession lined up on either side of the trench of red-hot charcoal and the chanting increased in volume. Then the dancers went single file to one end of the rectangle. Quite deliberately and with the same dancing gait, they strolled

nonchalantly across the red-hot coals as though they were not there. When the dancers reached the other side it was quite obvious that none of them had been burnt or appeared to have suffered in any way.

'How do they do it?' Vicky hissed.

'It's a trick!' Arthur mouthed.

'Hush! Don't give us away,' Ramon warned.

They waited until those taking part slowly moved on, then made their way to where the ashes of the charcoal remained. Even from the edge they could feel the heat coming up at them. They dared each other to walk on the cinders.

'Come on Arthur, show us how to do the trick,' begged Rosie.

He did not take up the challenge. Even Moses wisely kept at a safe distance.

'Uncle Roland might know how it is done, but if I ask him he'll guess that we have been here without permission. He seems to know everything,' Vicky told them.

They kept their escapade to themselves. It was only years later that they learnt that there were other fire-walkers throughout the world who claimed to do 'the trick' under hypnosis.

8

Caught

The second incident occurred three weeks later. Tree Tops was still very popular with the four, who were making it more and more cosy. They had also improved the access to their lookout post above so that they could more readily see anyone approaching their hide-out.

Sure enough, one day Rosie up in the Crow's Nest saw a lone rider by their side of the river, in view one minute and lost the next. There were rocks, ravines and brambles about and that part of the wood was only visited during the deer hunting season.

'There's a horse rider by the river, come and see . . . now he's dismounted and tied up his horse,' Rosie announced. 'Get the binoculars, I don't recognise him, it's too far away.'

Ramon joined her. 'Who can it be? On horseback too.'

'Perhaps it is one of Suzanne's workers come here by mistake,' queried Vicky.

'Perhaps she is meeting "a groom".' Arthur was still annoyed at Suzanne's remark. 'Where are the binoculars?'

Rosie passed them on.

'Yes, he is waiting, sitting on a rock,' Arthur said.

'Can I have a go?' Ramon was impatient. 'Yes I can see someone, I don't know . . . a man is coming on foot to meet him.'

'My turn,' said Vicky. 'Where? Yes it's a boy; I think I've seen him before.'

'Then I must know him too, let me see,' asked Arthur. 'Fishy! Very fishy! The boy just gave the man a bundle . . . and now the man looks as if he's giving the boy some . . . what are they up to? Now they're going off.'

'What's it all about? What are they selling or buying here?' asked Rosie.

'I don't know but we can try to find out, we can be detectives,' said Ramon excitedly.

'But where do we start?' Arthur asked.

'I know!' Vicky stated. 'The first thing we do is to find out if anybody around here has lost anything. If they have, we can tell Uncle what we have seen. If not, we look out for these two at the same spot just in case they turn up again.'

'You're right, Vicky, if they turn up again they'll do so at the same time here next week, it's possible!' said Arthur speculatively. 'We'll keep a look out here and two of us can get nearer in case we need to challenge them. Can you whistle yet, Rosie?'

'Of course I can, I've been practising. I can even imitate a bird, listen to me.' She gave a demonstration and was very pleased with herself.

'Let's start by asking Flo and Milly if anything is missing in the house, then we'll try Gran's.'

The maids had not noticed anything unusual. But later that afternoon Cook realised that some pure silver coffee spoons were missing from the kitchen dresser and six silver tea spoons had gone from Gran's kitchen. They had to enlist the help of Uncle Roland.

'Well done, children,' he praised them. 'But we mustn't jump to conclusions. You'd better let me play detectives with you too. You think the man and the boy might meet again next Saturday if there is more loot?'

'Yes,' Rosie told him. 'When I see them from the hide, I'll whistle. Vicky and Arthur will be nearer their meeting place to see more clearly what they are exchanging and –'

'I'd better be there with you. I don't want you to be in any danger. I'm going to have to let the police know that we are suspecting the two.'

Reluctantly, the children agreed. The man did not come the next Saturday and in some way the youngsters were disappointed. But the following week, there he was. Rosie felt the weight of responsibility heavily on her young shoulders when it was time for her to whistle. She tried as hard as she could but no whistle would come out. She nearly cried in dismay, but then the thought crossed her mind that Ramon would think girls were useless and he had better find a boy instead as a special friend.

She steadied herself and – hoorah – out came the whistle. Uncle Roland and Arthur pounced on the man and Vicky and Ramon on the boy. There was only a brief tussle with the man but the boy was wiry, agile and as slippery as an eel. He wriggled and streaked off but he had reckoned without Moses who chased him, caught his trousers and hung on until the children arrived and overpowered him.

They marched the man and the boy to the villa and telephoned Inspector Dunville who sent his sergeant at once to collect them.

It turned out that the boy called at kitchens with eggs and fruits to sell and then asked for a drink of water. Then there was invariably a disturbance outside which the cook or maid went to investigate, giving the boy time to steal something of value. The man had an arrangement with the boy to meet him at some quiet place at regular intervals to off-load the goods in exchange for cash. The four 'detectives' were praised by the police because the thieves had been active on other estates as well, using the same technique.

From that time on they kept up a regular watch from the Crow's Nest but, apart from some very interesting birds, they saw nothing else of such magnitude again. But for a long time afterwards they told their friends how they'd caught thieves red-handed on their estate.

9

Roger

The friends spent much of their spare time together and met after school to do their homework at the long table under the watchful eyes of one of their aunts. But sometimes they were forced to separate when they received visitors or were themselves invited elsewhere.

One such time had arrived. Vicky and Rosie's second cousin, Roger, and his sister, Emma, were coming to spend a few days on the estate. They lived in a house just outside the city and their father was a government official. Vicky and Rosie thought their cousins were 'stuck-up' because they refused to play with any other children on the estate whom they called 'the servants'.

As someone who comes from 'the big city', Roger was also infuriatingly superior and calculating. He was always saying to Vicky, 'When we are married, Vicky, I will not let you talk to these servants as equals otherwise they won't respect you. You should talk only to "proper" friends.'

'Marry you, Roger? Why don't you drop dead! I'll never marry you,' she fumed.

He looked pleased when he annoyed her. 'Of course we will marry, silly girl. Mother says money marries money, then it stays in the family. I shall inherit a grand house in the city and you and Rosie, De Vere Domaine. We can spend most of our time in the city and a few months here with all our children.'

Vicky's answer was to saddle her horse and ride away.

The cousins arrived and were greeted warmly by the adults. Roger, at fifteen, had shed most of his puppy fat and now looked darkly handsome. His green eyes lit up at the sight of Vicky and if she had not turned her head just in time she would have received his kiss on the lips. Everyone was amused except for her. Emma, in comparison to her brother, was a little mouse. Rosie always felt sorry for her and gave her much attention.

Both cousins were very good at playing cards and chess and so much of the week they spent indoors. They also rode quite well, having learnt on the estate when they were younger. They enjoyed riding round De Vere Domaine and being greeted like royalty by the workers. Somehow, they never knew why, one day their horses took them to the tree house.

'What's that?' asked Emma.

'We spend a lot of our time up there at weekends and during the holidays, it's not the sort of thing you would like,' said Rosie.

'No, I don't like heights,' stated Roger. 'Any height gives me vertigo,' he continued, making it sound as if it were a most desirable thing to have.

'It looks mysterious,' murmured Emma. 'What have you put inside the house? I'd love to see.'

Rosie said, 'Oh, lots of things to make it cosy: a carpet, curtain, a table, cushions . . . things . . . private . . . games . . . look I'll show you if you wish, don't be

afraid, put a foot here like this, I'll help you.'

'It's rather private,' Vicky wanted them to understand.

'Private? What are you hiding?' asked Roger. 'Cigarettes, I bet. Well if Emma can climb . . . look she's nearly there, then I can.'

Defiantly he followed in Emma's steps with Vicky encouraging him only half-heartedly.

The cousins admired Tree Tops ungrudgingly. The girls treated them to biscuits and lemonade which they always kept in the house. But when it was time to go down Roger froze and could not bring himself to do it whatever the three girls said or did to make him. Eventually they gave up and went to fetch two workmen who had to carry him down bodily. The girls laughed and teased him mercilessly.

So the next day he sulked and refused to play tennis. The others begged him, as a threesome was harder. But once the game was over the players felt hot and Roger agreed to go for a swim in the river pool. He took great care to hide behind a bush to change, feeling rather conscious of the whiteness of his skin compared to his cousins' sunburnt colour.

'Hurry up, Roger,' Emma shouted joyously. 'It's nice, there's no one here to look at you.'

'How do you know? I heard a noise . . .' he said.

When he thought no-one was looking Roger ran into the water and thankfully hid his whiteness. The water was a clear luminous green and soon Roger forgot his bashfulness. They slid, they dived, aquamarine droplets clinging to them like shimmering sequins. They enjoyed themselves for a good hour.

It was time to change before going back to the villa when Roger, aghast, screamed, 'I can't find my clothes. It's Moses, he must have taken them, the mongrel!'

'No!' Rosie pointed out that Moses had been in and out of the water with them most of the time fetching his ball. 'He does not take clothes, you must have left them somewhere else, we'll help you find them.'

They searched but could not find them. There was nothing for Roger to do but to walk back to the villa in his wet trunks and pale skin.

'You've told me there are thieves on these estates, I can't believe they even steal clothes!' Roger was furious.

As they were walking up the steps, Flo came to meet them.

'Your clothes are here, Mr Roger; Cook heard a knock at the kitchen door and somebody had left your clothes there.'

'Did Cook see who it was?' asked Roger.

'No, we didn't see anybody . . . sorry!'

The girls also apologised. Later, when Vicky saw the glint in Cook's eyes, she guessed who the culprits were.

10

The Invitation

The friends missed each other more if one or two of them actually left the estate to visit or went on holiday. They promised each other then to record everything they did so that they would share their experiences on their return.

The Aunts Beatrice and Charlotte and Uncle Roland had been invited to a long weekend for the twenty-fifth wedding anniversary of their friends, the Robinsons, who lived some twenty miles up north on another estate. The celebrations were to last three days; twenty-four people were going to be present, fifteen to sleep, the others coming every day. Uncle Roland at once said he would not leave the estate, he had too much to do; the aunts announced that all the jollities at the Robinsons would be too much for them. 'Definitely, not our cup of tea!' as they put it. It was decided by the family that Victoria, at the age of thirteen, was grown up enough to represent the De Veres and she could take as a suitable present an antique silver candelabra.

Vicky swelled with pride at the honour and was even

more pleased when she was put on the train with a suitcase full of beautiful new clothes which had been hastily bought.

When she returned on the Monday the boys and Rosie could not wait to hear how she had spent her time away from them.

'When the train arrived at the station on Friday morning, she began, 'the three younger Robinsons were there to meet me, the twins, Maggie and Jennie, who are eighteen and both engaged to be married and their brother James who is sixteen. Their hospitality from that moment was incredible. I was made to feel that I was the most important guest to have come. Their estate is not far from Port Lewis and their villa looks more like a ranch. The house was already full of people and more people were expected. I was shown to my room, which I was to share with a girl called Claire who is a year older than me. That afternoon some of us went out to play tennis or croquet but then we were told at five o'clock that everyone was going to have to play rounders.'

'Rounders?' asked Arthur. 'Unbelievable!'

'Not everybody wanted to play but the Robinsons did not mind who you were; fat or thin, old or young, they tried to make you join in. It was hilarious! Only when it was dark did we go in. A cold buffet supper was ready for people to eat after they had changed. James was surrounded all the time by a group of young girls, including Claire who seemed to be crazy about him.'

'Were you?' Arthur interrupted.

'No fear, he's nice but too old for me, but I liked him,' she said.

'Anyway, after dinner James picked up a little bell, rang it very formally and after telling us that breakfast would be early, he warned us that it would be followed by a treasure hunt.'

'A treasure hunt?' This time Ramon was incredulous.

'Yes and it was great fun. We set off with our instructions; I was with the Robinsons and Claire. They gave us such a lot of help with the clues, directions and all that. We kept meeting other guests and putting them off the scent. It was so amusing and such fun. But by the end, all the guests had found a bottle of perfume or rum as treasure and at every stage we found a bag of sweets to eat, just in case we had missed breakfast, I suppose. I truly don't understand how they made it so that every group won.'

'By giving them all different instructions,' Arthur explained. 'Go on . . .'

'Straightaway, the men went hare and rabbit hunting. We, the ladies went into town shopping. There we whizzed in and out of shops, looking at the latest dresses, hats and bags. Then we were taken to the jewellers where the twins had chosen their engagement rings.'

' "What about a little semi-precious ring for these two pretty young ladies?" asked Mrs Robinson of the jeweller and she made me and Claire choose a small ring each, look.'

'I wish I had come,' said Rosie dreamily.

'Pretty!' Arthur said curtly.

'Very nice,' from Ramon. 'Then?'

'We were booked at the Plaza Hotel for a late lunch, "something light," Mrs Robinson said. This was a salmon mousse, followed by a steak and salad and a sweet trolley with delicious patisseries, creamy cakes, éclairs, profiteroles, sponge fingers, chocolate gateau – I forgot scones and jam – and to finish almond ice cream.'

'Yum, you make us feel hungry,' commented the boys.

'Well, the treat was not over. It turned out that the Robinsons had tickets for the matinée performance of *Madame Butterfly*. The singers came from Paris and they were excellent. The music was nice but the story sad, about a Japanese girl and a French sailor.'

'What did you do afterwards?' Ramon was eager to know.

'I was so tired and so full of food, I was excused and had an early night. But I could hear music and dancing dimly through the night. I was glad I did not stay up all night because Sunday was "the day" we were told.'

'How do they top all that?' Arthur asked.

'Well, they had a picnic prepared. Early in the morning, servants were putting hampers, crates, baskets, plates and all that to fill two vans. Then the boots of those who came by car were filled too. By twelve it was ready and we set off like a military convoy – guess where?'

'They live near the capital and not far from Coconut Beach, so you went to the beach?'

'Wrong! That's where I thought we were going but the road was getting rougher and rougher and higher and twisting and then we reached it . . . The Robinsons' hunting lodge. You can't see it until you're almost upon it and yet it's there on raised ground and from it you get a marvellous view of the forest. The food was taken from the vehicles. There was everything, a whole cooked ham, smoked salmon, roast beef, chickens, venison, bread and rice and macaroni, crates of wine, beer, lemonade, cheeses of all sorts and a gigantic twenty-fifth wedding anniversary cake. The speeches were made here in the lodge and we had pink champagne for the toast.'

'Did you dance or play there?' Arthur asked.

'No, no dancing, it would have frightened the deer and any wild life. After the meal we sat on the verandah quietly from where you could see, if you were lucky, the stags as they crossed the paths. Some people went for a quiet stroll in the woods. The Robinsons were so welcoming, I had a great time.'

'You obviously did not give us a thought, did you?' Arthur wanted to know.

'Sorry, I . . .'

'Don't bother to pretend . . . say, Vicky, these friendly people, these generous people, would they have welcomed Ramon and me?'

Sadly she shook her head.

'I don't mind, I wouldn't go anyway,' said Ramon.

'I tell you what!' Arthur was angry and very jealous. 'I'll go to America one day and make my fortune. Then I'll come back and show all these friends of yours.'

As he stormed away Vicky shouted after him, 'You're my best friend . . .'

She did not know if he had heard.

Holidays

Every year, during the hot season, the De Vere family spent at least a month by the sea on the eastern part of the island. This year Mrs De Vere had bought a larger cottage from a friend on the south western side of the island. The girls were getting very excited indeed at the idea of staying in a new place at Broad Bay.

Vicky and Rosie talked about the preparations which were going on. Arthur could not help saying, 'You are off again. It won't be the same here without you for so long. No games, no tennis. Can we look after the horses, are you taking Moses with you?'

Ramon added, 'We've only been to the beach a couple of times when Dad was alive, I can't remember much about it.'

The girls were struck dumb. It had never occurred to them that everybody did not spend weeks at a time at the seaside.

They knew, of course, that the boys were poor but how poor? They were always famished, and Tessa told them that boys were greedy and she made sure there was extra food in the picnic baskets for the girls to share. In return the boys collected fruits from higher branches for the Cook to make jam. What they had in the way of clothes and shoes obviously came from the secondhand shop at the Monastery. They had no games and borrowed tennis racquets and balls. On the other hand Vicky and Rosie had so much and they took it all for granted.

'Life is unfair,' Vicky told her sister. 'What can we do to get the boys a seaside holiday? Who do we ask?'

'Let's try Aunt Bee, she's kind to them during homework,' Rosie said.

Victoria cornered Aunt Beatrice. 'I'm sad, Aunt Bee, do you realise that Arthur and Ramon have only been to the seaside once or twice when their father was alive and never to stay? They are such special friends, I mean on the estate,' she was quick to add. 'We are so much alike, we do everything together and we never quarrel. I do wish they could come with us. After all, no-one knows us in the new place. The maids come, Tessa comes. If the boys came they can help fetch and carry wood, light the camp fires and do the barbecues. We can help too . . . please?'

Aunt Bee smiled. 'What a speech . . . you help? what a joke! In the kitchen? Cook would have a fit! I don't suppose Mrs Benoit will allow her sons to come. Perhaps if I say that I'll help you all revise your school work! I do admit that they have done all their home-work extremely well. I'll have a word with their mother when I do my teaching rounds, then I'll tackle your mother . . . although I must say I am surprised she has allowed you to be friends with them for so long . . . to be white and poor is a sin on this island.'

'They can't help it and why can't we choose our friends? We like Arthur and Ramon and we don't like

Roger and Emma much, yet they come to stay with us . . . please, Aunt Bee.'

'Roger and Emma are related to us and we are all members of the same "club" which the boys cannot join because they can't afford it,' stated her aunt.

To the girls' delight and surprise Aunt Bee had no problems arranging for the boys to come. Mrs De Vere would have invited Roger and Emma but they were going to Europe this summer on an educational tour. She did not want the children to become bored and she did not have time to find more suitable guests.

Mrs Benoit welcomed the idea of having some free time to herself when she could go and visit relatives in town.

'Rosie, let's catch the boys and tell them the good news ourselves.' They waited for them as they were going home.

'Arthur, Ramon, *you are invited* to spend three weeks with us at the seaside,' the girls shouted.

As expected, the boys jumped for joy.

12

Seaside

The girls marvelled at the delight and wonder the boys showed at what they had taken so much for granted. So the sea became more blue, the sand more white and the large waves crashing over the reef less threatening and dark.

The friends spent hours in the sea or exploring the rocks and sand dunes. At low tide they walked to the reef and discovered its delights: the coral alive, the small multi-coloured fish darting in and out, the sea anemones shimmering and inviting their prey with enticing fingers.

Vicky became poetical. 'It's an underwater museum, a world of enchantment . . . We'll teach you how to handle crabs so they don't nip you. Then the special way to catch a small octopus. You hold it by the head and then turn it inside out before it has time to release its ink. It can't see and you put it in the bucket.'

'You must be joking!' laughed Ramon.

'When Uncle comes he'll help me identify all the creatures for my school topic,' said Rosie.

The reef acted as a barrier from the deep sea, the

ocean beyond. There they could see dolphins playing, jumping in and out of the water, swirling, plunging, arching themselves as if to show off to them. Once, in this great expanse of sea, Arthur pointed to a large black shape down below like a shadow and they agreed it could have been a shark or a marlin.

As the holiday progressed the children became stronger and muscular and their swimming and diving improved. Aunt Bee kept a benevolent eye on them and was always ready to answer their questions. After one exhausting day they were grouped around a camp fire after watching an orange sunset. Tessa was singing a tum-tum song and then she stood up and started to dance, waggling her bottom from side to side. Both Milly and Flo joined her. The children followed suit in a conga line, going faster and faster until they all tumbled on the sand, laughing and horseplaying happily.

'Let's tell ghost stories? Shall we?' asked Vicky.

'Rosie will get frightened and keep us awake.' Aunt Bee was worried.

'No, I won't. I don't believe in ghosts anyway and I know a good story to tell,' said Rosie.

'Good! In the end we'll vote on which one was the most scary,' Ramon decided.

Each one in turn tried to be more frightening by acting and with sound effects. At last they voted. Ramon had made the correct suggestion because he won and Aunt Bee promised to buy him a present when they next went shopping in the local market.

'This is heaven, Miss Bee,' Ramon said to her. 'I wish I could stay here for ever. We are having such a good time, all the food we can eat, the sea is lovely, the rocks, the games, I like it all. I want to make a wish that we stay together in this place for ever and ever. As soon as I see a shooting star, I shall wish . . .'

'I think Ramon is right, this is heaven on earth. I would not mind staying here. What do you say, Vicky?' Arthur asked.

'Agreed! Let's stay,' Vicky was quite willing.

Aunt Bee explained. 'You are happy because it is all new to you. Do you know that Mother has bought this place because we were getting bored with the old cottage in East Bay?' She was addressing the boys.

'I'd never get bored here,' Ramon was adamant.

'I'll show you a place on the top of Mount Charmanet, one of the most isolated parts of the island, which used to be a paradise. Legend has it that a tribe lived there and they had everything but they got bored. I'll tell you the story, Ramon,' promised Aunt Bee.

'Are we going there? When?' enquired Ramon.

'Let's get ready tomorrow and go the day after. Now it's time for everybody to go to bed.'

'Can somebody come with me in the dark? I'm scared,' said Rosie.

'Rosie is a baby! Rosie is a baby!' they chanted.

13

Charmanet Legend

True to her word, Aunt Bee organised an expedition to the top of Mount Charmanet with its famous multi-coloured sand dunes. She decided that the party would leave early to avoid the sun and go on foot by the path which curved gently towards the flat summit. In late afternoon Fred would come in the station wagon by the longer tourist road to pick them up.

Well equipped with haversacks full of food, they walked in Indian file through sugar cane fields to reach the winding path at the foot of a hill leading to Mount Charmanet. Steadily and quietly they climbed until half-way up they reached a vista point.

From this spot they could see miles of the magni-ficent coastline of the island in all its majestic splen-dour. The sight was breathtakingly beautiful: such a lovely sea, sky, shore and rock with no people to be seen. They had before them a vision of blue heavens, brown earth, green-blue sea and white foam touching to infinity.

'I feel we are the only persons alive on earth at the moment,' Vicky said as she slipped her hand into

Arthur's. He pressed her hand. 'Yes we are, you and I will always be together. When we reach the top, we'll find a tree – our tree here – and we'll carve our initials on it and we'll always remember we were here on Mount Charmanet.'

Back on the climb through the rich forest, they came across a spring and drank its cool, fresh water. Now and again they startled a deer which bounded away. They caught sight of monkeys swinging, chattering and disappearing in the distance. They wondered what the grunting noises were which were being carried to them on the wind.

'Wild pigs, boars,' Aunt Bee explained. 'They don't usually attack unless their piglets are threatened.'

'How big are they?' Rosie wanted to know.

'Bigger than domestic pigs,' Aunt Bee answered.

At last they reached the top and suddenly burst into a clearing. Once more that day they were awestruck. For here, surrounded by the dark green of the forest, was a broad expanse of multi-coloured sand dunes gleaming under the sun. They formed a series of ridges in different tints, ranging from pale cream through reds to vivid purples.

'Like the colours of Joseph's coat,' exclaimed Rosie.

'Like a painter's palette,' added Ramon.

'It's fantastic . . . unbelievable,' said Arthur.

'Kaleidoscopic', said Vicky, thinking of a favourite toy of her childhood.

'Stop showing off, Vicky,' scolded Rosie.

Having overcome their surprise and pleasure, they ran here and there, marvelling at the coloured sands.

'Are there other places like this in the world?' asked Vicky of Aunt Bee.

'No, not quite,' she replied. 'These dunes were caused by volcanic eruptions on the island in the

78

distant past. The sand came from under the sea as well as the mountain. For some reason the different colours never mix. You can make the experiment by taking a few colours on the edge of the dunes and mixing them. Perhaps they will have separated before we leave this evening. The curious thing about the sands is that the surrounding forest never spreads onto them. Scientists have complicated explanations for it, but to me it's simply magic! Anybody ready for food?'

They were ravenous and had a hearty picnic lunch in the shade of a jacaranda tree. Victoria and Arthur strolled a little further off and looked for a tree they could both climb. With Arthur's penknife they carved their initials together with a heart joining them. They looked at each other and suddenly felt too shy to speak. They slipped down the tree and rejoined the others.

After a while Aunt Bee stretched and yawned. 'I've given you some of the facts about the sand dunes. There is also the legend I talked about, told me by my late Aunt Andrée Poilly. Would you like to hear it now, Ramon?'

'Oh, yes please,' they chorused.

'Once upon a time, soon after the world began, there was a tribe of people who lived on the top of this mountain where we are now. They were the chosen people, selected by St Jacques to be his children, for him to love and even to spoil. They were a handsome and healthy, contented people who revered St Jacques. The adults of the village spent their days gardening and looking after their village, preparing good meals and teaching the children. The children liked to learn. They also loved sports and they all followed artistic pursuits. The tribe made pottery, they

painted pictures, they wove beautiful material and they sewed clothes. In the evenings they met in the village square to play music, to sing songs, to tell and to listen to stories and to act plays and play games.

'Twice a year the elders had meetings to discuss their affairs and future needs. Then the chief would call St Jacques to ask him for advice and to provide them with all the things they needed.

' "It is time to send for St Jacques. Beforehand let us remember to give thanks that we are here in this garden of paradise. Look at the trees covered with fruits and the bushes with flowers, listen to the sound of the clean, crystal-clear water falling over the rocks. See the butterflies, bees, birds and dragon flies. We are blessed! Thank heaven for our paradise!"

'The summoning of St Jacques was a cause for a great celebration. The chief went to the shrine and removed from the altar the long, silver trumpet. He put it to his lips and played a soulful tune followed by three long blasts. At once St Jacques appeared in the sky on his golden chariot, drawn by three white horses. Everyone shouted and waved until St Jacques landed and alighted from the chariot.

'Then followed feasting and dancing until no-one could eat or move any more. In the end St Jacques granted all their wishes, climbed on his chariot and disappeared into the clouds leaving everybody happy . . . except one.

'Young Rollo felt restless after the party was over. Instead of going to rest or play like the others, he decided to go hunting. But he ignored the deer he could have killed very easily to take home to cook and instead went further down the mountain where they were all forbidden to go. No-one was allowed to leave Paradise Garden. This was a rule which must not be broken. Now Rollo had done it.

'His heart pounded strongly when he heard voices. He was frightened and wanted to run back home but his feet were glued to the ground. He was lucky a rock shielded him from view. At the same time he was burning with curiosity and had to know who were the people that he could hear. Did they look and behave the same as the members of his tribe?

'Why hasn't St Jacques mentioned them to us? he wondered. What is he hiding from us?

'His racing heart was fit to break. He saw two women coming from the forest. They were balancing large bundles of firewood on their heads. He noted with astonishment that one was also struggling with a small child strapped on her back. With swaying hips, they were going past his rock when he heard one say clearly, "My life is full of MISERY, sheer MISERY!"

'The other added "Mine, you can say, is also full of MISERY and of POVERTY!"

'As soon as they had gone, Rollo climbed back up the mountain. His friends greeted him with, "Where have you been? We missed you. What is wrong with you, you look flushed?"

' "Come here and listen . . . I've got something important to tell you."

'They came closer.

' "I've been where it is forbidden to go, I left the Garden for a while . . ."

'A gasp went up from the circle of faces gaping at him.

' "You know how the elders and St Jacques tell us this is paradise, that we are the chosen people and have got everything. Well, it is a lie!"

'Another greater gasp came from the crowd and, pleased with himself, Rollo carried on after a slight

83

pause for effect. "There are other people down there and I have seen two women and a child with my own eyes."

'They looked at each other in disbelief.

' "I tell you I have seen them and heard them talk."

'Third gasp.

' "And they've got things that we've never been given. One is MISERY and the other is POVERTY."

' "I want some," a youth cried at once.

' "Me, too," shouted the others.

'They started to chant, "We want some, we want some . . ." and they marched towards the meeting place.

'When the chief heard what Rollo had to say he was sad. He knew that he would have to summon St Jacques again to explain the emergency caused by Rollo's disobedience. Now so many people in the tribe were asking for some misery and poverty that he had no choice. He sounded the trumpet.

'A surprised St Jacques descended and listened to the elders. Then he asked to speak to the youngsters. At last he lifted both hands skywards and said, "You have broken the cardinal rule and now you want something which was denied you – so be it! I have loved you very much as a father who wants the best for his children. In memory of the good times we have shared together and before I leave you for ever, I shall give you one last present. Whenever you see my gift, you will think of me."

'There was a flash of lightning followed by a clap of thunder and a cloudburst. At the same time the sun shone, causing a resplendent rainbow to fill the sky. Its end touched the ground where they stood and where we are now and turned the earth into dunes of multi-coloured sands on which no vegetation would ever grow again. The colours were so splendid that for a minute everyone cheered.

'St Jacques clapped his hands and they heard dreadful grunts coming from the woods.

' "Goodbye, you will soon know about misery and poverty," he said and left them.

'Next, wild boars with fierce tusks and small evil eyes appeared from the woods. Whilst the tribe stood rooted to the spot with horror the boars overturned everything in their way. They slashed at the villagers' legs with their tusks. The people screamed, ran here and there but there was no escape. Trapped, they had no choice but to take to the trees with the boars surrounding them, looking up with malevolent eyes.

'Years passed but the chosen people could not regain their paradise. Everything they had was destroyed. They could not come down from the trees and the old ones died. The young eventually grew tails and learnt to swing from tree to tree and to eat fruits to stay alive. For a long time they kept calling "St Jacques . . . Jacques . . . Oh . . ." They are still called Jackoes on the island. Today you have seen their descendants; they are the monkeys you pointed out this morning and you heard the wild boars grunting in the forest.'

'I hope the monkeys are no longer miserable,' Rosie said sadly.

Ramon questioned, 'Miss Bee, the story is saying that a young man became bored with paradise. Why? When he had everything he wanted?'

'I suppose,' said Aunt Bee, 'it is human nature that the more we have, the more we want. We are never satisfied for long with what at first may seem like heaven. But we are not like that, are we? Are you, girls?'

85

At that moment the station wagon turned up to drive them zigzagging down the mountainside. They'd had a fantastic day.

14

Mournful Rock

The arrival of Uncle Roland and Aunt Charlotte was greeted with enthusiasm by the children. Their activities took on a different tempo. The girls boasted that Uncle Roland was an expert boatman and fisherman as well as an excellent shot. Straight away he wanted to go deep sea fishing and was prepared to take the boys with him. Victoria pleaded to go but got nowhere. They were afraid that she or Rosie would be seasick on the high waves and would want to return before the big fish had been caught. The girls were not pleased. They knew they could do whatever the boys did. The day seemed endless before the men returned. Their catch had been good and included a good size tuna and a large marlin. It was the boys' turn to relate what had happened:

'There was a lot of waiting, you need tons of patience – Ramon even fell asleep,' Arthur was feeling important.

'No, I didn't, I was only pretending,' Ramon protested.

'Then when you get a bite, you come to life, you

have to learn how to play the fish, how to reel in with all your strength. It's not a girl's hobby, definitely not. Look at the size of this tuna, this marlin and we nearly caught a baby shark . . . but it got away!'

On the Sunday Uncle Roland took the four to the reef. Their uncle, with dexterous seamanship guided the boat through a gap in the coral into a narrow channel. He showed them how over millions of years the skeletons of tiny sea animals had built up the coral structure from the base of the ocean to form the mass of limestone which created the reef. Where they were it was razor sharp and in no way should they or anyone else attempt to swim near the reef. If they did they would be dashed by the waves against the coral and would be cut to pieces, becoming good feed for the sharks. But they could catch smallish fish and shrimps with a net if they were lucky.

On the way back Uncle Roland stopped at a deep lagoon where he knew it would be safe for them to swim and to dive from the boat. In and out of the boat they went, first seeing who could skim dive the furthest then who could dive the deepest. There was not much in it. The girls had more experience but the boys were certainly stronger. In the end they were worn out and ready to go back.

'Do people dive from that black rock sticking out into the sea?' Ramon asked.

'Definitely not,' was the answer from Uncle Roland. 'The rock is called Mournful Rock and is very high and slippery. There is a story about the rock which I can tell you tonight. We'll have a camp fire and grill the fish and the shrimps we caught today. Then I'll tell you.'

Uncle Roland pulled slowly on the oars taking them back to the shore. 'I must teach you to row, boys,' he said.

'Yes, please!' they agreed.

'Let us have a go, we know how to row,' said Rosie.

'Next time!' Uncle Roland promised.

Back ashore they had little time to get the fire going before the sun set. They grilled their fish and shrimps, put potatoes in the ashes to bake and, once ready, smothered them with butter to eat. They had a feast. Rosie could not wait for the meal and the singsong that followed to be over. She wanted to hear the story of the Rock. Uncle Roland duly obliged.

'Beatrice has told you the legend of the mountain, but the story of Mournful Rock is only part legend and mostly based on fact,' he said.

'Once upon a time slaves were kept on the island to work on the sugar cane. It is difficult now to accept the idea of slavery but, remember, there were slaves in many parts of the world only a century ago and that most of the masters were good and kind and treated their slaves well. They gave them food and shelter and looked after their health so that they could work better for them. However, some of the owners were harsh and cruel and they were sometimes so terrible that the slaves found life intolerable and ran away. They hid in the forests and near marshes where it was difficult to reach and find them. If they could hide far enough away and find food, they survived. Some were hunted down by posses of men and dogs. Once they were caught the slaves were flogged and perhaps even shot.

'One of these runaway slaves, called Ben, came along the seashore to the foot of Mournful Rock, so sheer and forbidding. He was so determined not to be found that somehow he succeeded, by risking his life, to climb the rock. Then carefully and painstakingly, he hid the foot and handholds which he had made. He discovered that he could live on the rock, as he was able to collect rainwater and there was fish in the sea and game in the forest. So he went back to the forest and marshes to find other fugitives like himself and asked them to join him. Eventually there was a group of runaway slaves managing to survive on the rock. They sheltered in caves on the rock. At night they went back to the forest to find fruit and roots and set traps for animals. Unfortunately, at times they were so desperate for necessities like string, matches and clothes that they raided shops in out-of-the-way villages. Had it not been for this they might have been forgotten. But once shopkeepers complained of losing goods and money the masters had an excuse to organise posses of men and get police help to comb the forest for the runaways. At last they worked out where the slaves were hiding. The masters then had several meetings to organise a sort of military operation to recapture the slaves.

'The man in charge, called Colonel Blais, was cruel and self-important, with big bulging eyes in a bright pink face. He was an enormous man who loved to tower over his slaves and frighten them. Now he could not wait to get hold of the runaway slaves to punish them.

'To his annoyance, just as he was ready to put his plans into operation, a national decree proclaimed the end of slavery. From that day all slaves had become free men and women and nobody was allowed to keep slaves any more. Slaves all over the island rejoiced. But after the first excitement was over the newly freed slaves wished that their runaway friends could be given the good news too. They elected a leader who went to the authorities to ask them for the pardon of the runaways and for their freedom. The authorities

90

agreed. They asked Colonel Blais, who had a plan ready, to find the runaways and they sent along a small group of soldiers to help him and to give the slaves the good news.

'The slaves on the rock saw Colonel Blais coming and they recognised him at once. Then they saw the soldiers firing in the air to attract their attention and realised that their hide-out was discovered. They believed at once that they were going to be arrested and, knowing Colonel Blais, that they would be shot. Rather than go through that agony and having lost all hope, one after the other, they jumped to their deaths on the rocks below. A few of them had never been able to rid themselves of their chains and these can still be seen at the base of the rock at low tide. Ever since that time the rock has been known as the Mournful Rock.'

15

Water Spirit

There were not many days of their magical holiday left and it was Aunt Charlotte's turn to offer one last treat. She called the children over and asked, 'Would you like to go camping for two nights?'

'Yes please!' They were unanimous.

'Good, I'll take you on a mystery tour. Get your things together and organise yourselves for three days camping; decide who is going to collect wood, who cooks first, who washes up and so on. Get a rota arranged. Fred will drop us and the gear about one mile from the camping site. There's a lot of equipment and the tents to take so make sure you carry only necessities, but you will need your swimming things.'

They prepared their luggage with great anticipation and all was ready by the following morning. Once satisfied, Aunt Charlotte asked Fred to take them on their journey. The children had expected to be taken to some beach but Fred drove them inland for about half an hour towards the woods, where he left them. The trek to the site was steep and they were all perspiring profusely when they heard the tinkle of water not too far away. Steadily the sound of water increased. They quickened their pace, despite the heat, and the path led them to a pool at the bottom of a very tall waterfall.

'Can we jump in straightaway, Aunt Lotte?'

'Yes, it's quite safe, but just remember that the middle of the pool is extremely deep, don't try to stand there.'

In a few minutes they were all in the cool, clear water.

The waterfall came from a great height so that the water foamed as it hit the rocks below and created a cloud of coloured mist that shimmered and caused a vivid rainbow. As the water ran down the rocks it calmed and slid gently into a circular pool which was ideal for swimming.

'Let's see if we can find out how deep the pool is Arthur?' Vicky said.

'How?' asked Ramon. 'By counting to see how long we stay under?'

'No it would be better to take a piece of string straight down with us and then measure it when we come up. One of us holds the string and floats on top while the other dives.' Arthur thought this might work.

'Please let's count first and see for how long we can stay under,' Rosie asked.

'My go first.' Vicky dived in.

Arthur was getting worried by the count of thirty when her head popped up.

'It gets darker and darker, you can't see anything at all. I did not touch anything either. What was my count? Thirty? Who can beat that?'

Arthur went to forty-five and nearly burst a lung. Neither Rosie nor Ramon could do any better.

'Shall we try the string now? I'll go first again,' Vicky said.

They thought in the end that they had reached a depth of twenty six feet and there was still much further to go. They gave up.

They set up camp close to the pool. It took some time to pitch the tents but at last they had finished. They did not try to cook for a late lunch but ate bread, cheese and sardines this first day. The water was cool and delicious to drink.

'Let's explore to see if we can find any fruit,' said Aunt Charlotte after they had rested for a while. 'We can bring what we find back here to share.' As in many tropical forests, there was no shortage. They found bananas, guavas, breadfruit and a green pear-shaped fruit with a rather pungent smell. Arthur collected the heart of a palm, which was delicious in a salad. Back in camp they only had time to collect some wood and prepare the camp fire before the sun disappeared behind the trees.

'Story time Aunt Charlotte,' Rosie begged. 'You are the only one who has not told us a story yet.'

'True, I wondered when you would ask. Did you know,' she started, 'that this half of the island used to be dry and arid? It was covered by scrub, aloes and cacti and nothing else would grow, whilst on the other side of that mountain range over there the land was green and fertile. This waterfall did not exist and the river was dry for most of the year with only a trickle of water during the rainy season. Not many people chose to live on this side of the island. Yet there were stories of pirates' treasure being buried in these parts simply because there were so few inhabitants around to see them coming and going. Several people who believed these treasure stories dug here and there hoping to find a fortune. Others were tricked out of their money by bad men who mounted fake expeditions to find treasure. They pretended to have discovered maps and plans in caves and they sold shares in their expedition to the gullible.

'But one day a woman who was washing some clothing in a shallow pool in the river bed, scooped up a nugget of gold with a cloth. This caused a short-lived gold rush but no more gold was found. However, one of the gold seekers, a Mr Grant, was sure that he would eventually be successful and he bought some land here very cheaply. For years he searched for gold but as he was running out of money, he decided to supplement his funds by growing a crop that did not need too much water. The other day in the market you met his great-grandchild, Richard Grant, who is a rich planter growing pineapples and sugar cane on land which now has plenty of water. Mr Grant told me the story of his great-grandfather who was doing some gold prospecting, further up than we are now. He climbed up the hill, put up his tent and took out the few bits of equipment he had brought with him. Then he started to work until the sun went down and he was very weary. He cooked himself a meal and had only eaten a few mouthfuls when he fell asleep.

'He was woken up by someone calling his name. He opened his eyes and there stood before him an old man with a white beard down to his chest and long shoulder-length white hair. He was wearing a pale blue shirt, aquamarine trousers and he was wringing wet from head to toe.

"Good day to you stranger, you look drowned, has it been raining?" asked Mr Grant.

' "I am wet, weak and starving,' said the stranger ignoring the question.

' "You are welcome to eat what I have and you can take shelter in my tent. I welcome you, stranger, and I welcome the rain. We are suffering from the worst drought ever in these parts. Help yourself, I am going back to sleep.''

'He scarcely had time to see the stranger start to eat before he dozed off again. Just before he slept he thought he heard the old man say, "You will be rewarded for your kindness. Climb to the east until you find the spring and the boulder, there you will find the gold you seek."

'When Mr Grant woke up the next morning there was no sign of any stranger and no rain had fallen during the night.

' "Dreams, just dreams!" he told himself.

'He continued to pan for gold and then returned for breakfast to finish the food he had left the night before but all of it had been eaten and next to the pot was a very wet piece of cloth.

' "That's very odd, perhaps it wasn't a dream after all. I'd better go up eastwards and see if I can find the gold the old man mentioned near the spring and the boulder."

'He followed the course of the dry river bed and came across many boulders but never a spring. But at last he found an enormous rock practically hiding a cave. Nearby were greener bushes and a few lush trees which gave him a clue that perhaps he had found the spring.

'Sure enough, he found that the large boulder was causing most of the spring water emerging from the cave to be re-routed from this side of the mountain to the other side. Inside the cave it was dark and forbidding. He heard a drip, drip sound and, filled with exultation, he lit a torch. The brilliance that hit his eyes blinded him. His heart nearly stopped as he thought he had discovered an Aladdin's cave full of jewels glitter-

97

ing and sparkling. But when his wits came back to him and after blinking several times, he realised that what he was seeing was a cave full of glistening stalactites.

' "I have found the cave, I have found the boulder, but where is the gold?" Mr Grant asked himself.

'He spent another day looking for treasure in and around the cave without success. Downhearted he returned to his plantation. But that night the Old Man appeared in his dreams.

' "What is more important to you than gold, Mr Grant? What is it you need to give you and your men work?"

'Mr Grant suddenly woke up sweating.

' "WATER, WATER!" he shouted in the night, "We can have a river full of water. The Spirit of the Water was trying to tell me that water for me is LIQUID GOLD."

'Mr Grant returned to the cave and brought some of his plantation workers with him. They moved the boulder and water gushed out of the cave to feed both sides of the island, each having an equal share. Mr Grant started to grow pineapples on his land and as the land became more fertile he also grew bananas and sugar cane and he became a rich man.'

'At last a story with a happy ending,' said a sleepy Rosie. 'Can we go up to see if we can find the spring tomorrow?'

16

End of the Enchanting Holidays

The friends felt dejected because tomorrow they were going back home. They were walking along the beach, throwing pebbles to see who could get the most jumps on one skim. Moses was the only one full of beans, wanting and asking for more exercise, not knowing that the holidays were at an end.

'Let's walk to the Beak,' said Rosie.

This was the high promontory of rocks just in front of them which had, beyond it, a river pouring into the sea. It was no place to swim but they were fascinated to watch from the top the energy of the sea as it rushed at the rock and met the river head on, making eddies and whirlpools far out across the river mouth.

'Right,' said Arthur, throwing a stick for Moses to retrieve. 'I'll race Moses to the rocks, then you can throw him sticks.'

As the four neared the Beak, Arthur and Vicky flopped face down under a pine tree.

'It's over!' he said. 'The holidays have been wonderful, I wish they had been even longer.'

'I can't think of going back to normal life,' Vicky

carried on, 'or of school, can you? Two more years for us before the final exams. Already they are mentioning a European tour for me. I wonder if I might be allowed to have a career? Do you know Doc Dumas' daughter, Irene? She is determined to become the first woman doctor on the island.'

'I have read that women abroad become lawyers and even engineers!'

'I would be the first girl in my family with a career. All the girls I know only talk of getting married and having babies and which one will have more land or money, so tedious!'

'I . . .' started Arthur when a scream came from Rosie followed by, 'Come back, Moses!' and 'Stop, you fool!' from Ramon.

Both Arthur and Vicky leapt up and raced down to the sea. The crazy dog was swimming after the stick which had fallen by accident into the sea next to the Beak.

'Don't go in, Rosie, the tide is too strong,' yelled Vicky.

'Ramon, don't try anything silly,' shouted Arthur.

Helplessly they watched Moses, overtaken by his excitement and enjoyment, swimming behind the stick. Both were rapidly being taken by the current towards the tip of the Beak.

'He doesn't stand a chance if he gets caught in those whirlpools,' remarked Arthur sadly.

'Perhaps he'll get carried round the other side,' said Ramon hopefully.

'Please, please, we must go on top to find out,' cried Rosie.

They ran up the path which went round to the other side of the rock. By the time they got to the top there was no sign of Moses.

'If he had reached the other side of the river, the trees, the mangroves, or those rocks might have hidden him,' said Rosie as they looked about in despair.

'We have to go back and tell the others,' Vicky was in tears.

'We've lost him for good this time.'

'It was my fault,' sobbed Rosie. 'I did not throw the stick straight.'

'It was not your fault,' Ramon was adamant. 'It got carried by the wind.'

The sad group were trudging mutely back to the bungalow when they saw some fishermen returning to the landing stage as they did every day at that time.

'Hoy!' One was shouting at them, standing pre-cariously in the boat.

They stopped immediately.

'Is this yours?' he called holding up a very wet creature.

They ran to the landing stage as fast as tired legs could carry them and arrived as the boats came in. As soon as Moses saw them he jumped out of the fisherman's arms and came bounding up to them with excitement.

They all embraced him and didn't mind in the least getting drenched as he shook himself violently. The fisherman came over to explain what had happened.

'He was swimming strongly out to sea when I saw him and fished him out with the boat hook. He seemed to be quite keen to jump back in the sea as though he'd lost something and I had to hang on to him till we got here,' he said.

They thanked the man profusely and explained about the stick and they all heaved a great sigh of relief.

As they returned Vicky broke the silence. 'Another life, Moses!' she said.

The incident brought them down to earth and somehow made them accept that it was time to pack up for home before Moses found another stick in the water to chase.

17

Uncle Roland's Obsession

Horse racing was one of the islanders' passions and Uncle Roland took a keen interest in the sport and belonged to the island's racing club. Now for some reason, he became obsessed with the idea of winning the Gold Cup at the Champ de Mars. This racecourse had a mountain range as a backcloth and everyone was justly proud of it as a venue for any meeting of national importance.

Uncle Roland did not own any race horses and had therefore to start from scratch. So he went off to racing studs around the island looking for what he wanted, causing Gran De Vere to remark to the girls, 'Your father became obsessed in just the same way with planes and flying. He started to neglect the estate exactly as your uncle is doing at the moment, leaving the women to do a man's work. The sooner you take an interest in the running of the estate Vicky, the better.'

But the girls were also caught up with the fever and the anticipation of looking after and riding the two thoroughbreds Uncle Roland wanted to buy. When the horses eventually arrived on the estate, they fell in love with them straightaway. They were such handsome creatures, haughty, disdainful and giving of their best only after being treated like Hollywood stars.

Uncle Roland told his nieces, 'If you want us to win, spend as much time as you can helping to train De Vere One and De Vere Two. Guy, the trainer, will teach you anything you need to know about race horses but you must obey him completely.'

'Is that what you are going to call them Uncle, One and Two? How boring!'

'If you can come up with two winning names, I'll listen,' he laughed.

The four friends needed no further prompting and they each wrote down a long list of names. After much discussion, they came up with two unbeatable forces of nature, Tornado and Tempest, reminding them of their first meeting over two years ago.

'Good! Very Good!' accepted Uncle Roland at once. 'Yes, I think you have picked winners there all right!'

It became normal now for the four to wake up early enough to spend at least an hour mucking out, and fussing over Tornado and Tempest before going to school. Back home, their homework had to be finished faster than usual too, so they could be with the 'stars' before it got dark. To the girls' sorrow, Guy would not allow them to ride the horses.

'I have seen you ride, Misses Vicky and Rosie, and you ride well, but girls have a light touch and if the horses get used to it, they won't accept the hard pressures of the race course. Tornado and Tempest have to be ridden by men.'

The girls wanted to argue about this but Guy was the expert so they accepted it grudgingly. They were pleased they could help with the training sessions at the weekends when the trainee jockeys came. One Saturday, when the girls and the jockeys arrived a little later than usual, they saw Arthur and Ramon racing the horses. The girls were furious.

'You are not a good rider, Ramon, you know I am ten times better than you. How was it *you* were allowed to ride Tornado?!' Rosie asked fuming.

'We had the horses ready and Guy said we could have a go . . .' replied Ramon, trying to pacify her.

'It's not fair!' put in Vicky. 'Arthur, you're much too heavy for Tempest!'

'The horses were impatient, that's why we were allowed to start them off,' explained Arthur sheepishly.

'NOT FAIR!' shouted Rosie.

'No, definitely not fair!' said Vicky as Uncle Roland approached them.

'Eh! What's wrong, what's going on? I thought you four never quarrelled. I could hear you girls screaming from the other side of the paddock!'

'You let the boys ride the horses and you know they're not experienced, but you won't let us ride,' they said angrily.

Uncle Roland was taken aback by the strength of their reaction. 'I'm surprised at you. We just let the boys have a quick ride because the jockeys hadn't arrived. Anyway, you've been teaching the boys to ride ever since they came on the estate and now you say they're poor horsemen!'

'Sorry!' said Rosie, face down, 'I suppose I was really jealous.'

'Sorry! It's our first quarrel, isn't it, and it wasn't even your fault,' Vicky apologised to Arthur.

The decision rankled with the girls but at least the boys did not attempt to race the horses again. One

Sunday, when one of the trainee jockeys was sick, the girls returned to the attack.

'Please Uncle, let me have a go at racing Tornado,' begged Rosie. 'I'm lighter than Tim, I have watched him carefully and I can do anything he does.'

'All right, Rosie, it is better for you to do it than one of us and the horses shouldn't miss their training. Will she be all right, Guy?'

'Just this once perhaps. I know she rides well, but I won't allow it again.'

'I don't enjoy racing myself,' said Victoria, 'but Rosie is very good.'

Rosie needed no further encouragement. She ran across and mounted Tornado in one joyous leap and cantered off to join the other jockey, Ray, at the start. When the waiting group next saw them, both riders were flat out on the galloping horses. As the horses thundered past, everyone yelled with excitement as Rosie edged Tornado ahead, racing with great passion and panache. She eventually returned, exhilarated, to the cheers of the others. 'I can't wait to go home and tell Mum,' she said.

Minutes later she was bursting into the lounge.

'Mum, Gran, I can become a jockey,' she enthused. 'I rode like the wind on Tornado and I even beat Ray.'

'But I thought you weren't supposed to ride the racehorses,' said her Gran.

'Anyway, that's nonsense, girl, women don't become jockeys. It is far too undignified for women to race horses. The princesses Elizabeth and Margaret in England are good horsewomen but in public they ride side-saddle and they would never dream of racing in public.'

'How silly!' replied Rosie. 'Yet I can ride better than Tim and Ray,' and she swaggered off.

The time at last came for Uncle Roland to race his horses at the Grand Race Meeting of the year. Tornado and Tempest had been sent on a fortnight earlier so that they could get the feel of the course and also to enable Guy to keep an eye on the form of the other horses as they trained.

Uncle Roland wanted as many people as possible from the estate to cheer his horses. He reserved two carriages on the special Races Train on the day of the race. The first compartment was occupied by the De Vere family themselves but Gran De Vere would not come.

'Someone has to look after the estate otherwise everything will disintegrate about our ears . . .' she warned.

The more senior employees went in the carriage in which Arthur and Ramon also took seats whilst the second carriage was filled with the labourers and other workmen. The rest of the train was packed to the roof. The children found the thirty mile journey in the smoky steam train absorbing. They could faintly hear music and noisy laughter coming from the other carriages as their occupants already started celebrating. They did not open the windows, having been warned about soot floating from the engine and spoiling clothes. The station at Port Lewis was crowded and full of activity. The family took a taxi to the race course but the rest of the workers and the boys walked the short distance.

'I have never seen so many people in one place,' remarked Vicky, once they were on the racecourse. 'It's cram-full, really packed!' she said as they were pushed and jostled in the bright sunshine by the colourful crowd. Uncle Roland guided them towards the stands. The rest of the estate workers found their way to the field enclosure on the other side of the race track. The enclosure was a vast area of colour and moving humanity. Traders, under their multi-coloured umbrellas, were selling a number of exotic goods and the girls caught glimpses of tantalizing sweets as they wound their way through the throng.

Before they took their seats in the stands, the family passed the police band in their ceremonial uniforms, playing a selection of classical and popular music. Vicky and Rosie scanned the crowd but saw nobody they knew. Uncle Roland came over to them with programmes and they looked excitedly through the list to see where 'their' races were on the card. Eventually, the crowd started to thin as people made their way to their boxes or the railings for the first race.

'Look at all the people over there in the field enclosure,' Rosie said to her aunt. 'They are having such a good time, I wish I was there instead of here.'

'If you go there, you will get lost and you won't be able to see anything,' Aunt Charlotte told her.

'Can we go later Aunt Lotte?' Rosie persisted. 'I can see a woman selling coconuts. She is slitting the top, and look, you can see a child drinking the milk. Now she is halving the coconut and the child is eating the flesh. It looks delicious.'

'You are obviously hungry. We can have an excellent buffet lunch here, don't worry,' replied Aunt Charlotte.

But that was not what Rosie wanted. She was drawn towards the field where she could see the heaps of flowers, toys and sweets of all colours, lemonade in bottles with a marble in the top, funny hats, whistles and rattles. Traders were preparing food, then frying or grilling it on the spot. In the corner of the field was a fair and both girls were envious of those children riding on the merry-go-round and on the big wheel.

111

As the afternoon wore on, instead of following all the races, the girls kept focusing their binoculars on the milling crowds in the field enclosure but, however hard they scanned, they could not find Arthur or Ramon who were somewhere there swallowed up by the hordes of people.

Excitement mounted as their race was due to begin and it was Tempest's turn to race. There were eight horses in the race and although they cheered and cheered Tempest on, he only managed to come in third. Now it was Tornado's turn to try for the fourth race, the Gold Cup. Their enthusiasm grew as the horses came under starter's orders.

'Come on Tornado, you can do it,' they shrieked.

But to no avail; Tornado was not interested on that day and came in one but last.

'It's the jockey's fault,' proclaimed Rosie. 'He used too much whip. I know I would have done better.'

The whole family was disappointed but Uncle Roland was quite philosophical. 'Back to the drawing board,' was all he said.

The platform station was once more full for the last train home. It was evident that some people would have to spend the night in town.

'Thank goodness, we have booked carriages, Uncle,' Victoria said as she looked for the friends they had not seen all day. They were there waiting patiently with the others.

'There you are at last. Did you have a good time?' they were asking each other.

'I won a bet,' said Arthur, 'so I've bought you these orange sweets that you like and this . . .'

He handed Vicky a small rag doll dressed in a bright sarong.

'It's the nicest thing that's happened today,' Vicky

was touched. She just had time to say thank you before being separated in their different compartments.

.At that moment the station master came to have a word with Uncle Roland. A doctor and his wife needed to be back south that evening and were pleading for seats. Would Uncle Roland oblige as his carriage was not full.

Vicky at once suggested, 'Can Arthur and Ramon come here with us instead, please, Uncle Roland and let the strangers take their place?'

He agreed; he was thinking that he was tired after a long day and did not feel like making polite conversation with strangers.

The boys joined the girls and they started to share all their experiences of the day. Although they had been to see the same races on the same day, their experiences had been totally different and contrasted to a large extent. At the end, the girls confessed that they had longed to go to the field enclosure to join the boys and see the amusements and the boys had wondered what they were missing up there in the stands.

On that day they were made fully aware of the gulf between the lifestyle of the rich and the rest of the population.

As the train picked up its rhythm, everyone in the carriage fell asleep. After being apart all day, the four sat nearer to each other than they would have done normally. And once more Vicky surreptitiously slipped her hand into Arthur's, glad that they were together again.

18

The Birthday Party

This was going to be Victoria's last year at her present school. She wanted to pass the final exams and then to take decisions about her future. She was working harder at the moment, wishing that school was soon over and she could concentrate on her fifteenth birthday coming out party.

Already fashion magazines had been sent for and patterns shown to her. What fun! First she chose this dress, then that one. She had plenty of time to make sure exactly what sort of dress and what colour she wanted.

'Pale pink, perhaps,' she daydreamt, 'or peach with a very full skirt.'

She kept changing her mind. 'Everybody will wear a full skirt. I want to be different and have a fitting and slinky dress, that is if I am allowed.'

She started to draw a mermaid whilst in the middle of writing an English essay. 'This is no good at all. School work first and then I can give all my time and attention to the party.'

One evening as they were finishing their homework,

Aunt Charlotte said, 'Have you finished? Fine. Beatrice and I have just received the latest dance records we ordered from France and we are all going to learn and to practise the modern dances in time for your party. I heard that your cousins, Roger and Emma, already know them. Arthur and Ramon, you can help, it will be useful for you later when you go to your own parties.'

It did not take them very long to learn the dancing steps: slow, slow, quick, quick, slow. They glided to the music and learnt a slow foxtrot then a quickstep. They soon memorised the tunes, which were quite romantic. Arthur and Victoria danced together like proper partners, as if they had always danced together in that way. When a slow waltz was played, he held her a little more tightly and her body melted towards his and she thought that they were enchantingly in harmony with each other.

This was much nicer than holding hands and she rested her black curls on his shoulder, going all dreamy.

Aunt Beatrice interrupted abruptly. 'Arthur, you must dance with me, it's my turn to be led by a handsome young man who is now as tall as myself. Look at you!'

They laughed but Victoria felt a twinge of jealousy and then shame.

'Gracious me, I'm going funny in the head,' she told herself and then aloud, 'Ramon can dance with Aunt Lotte and I shall lead Rosie.'

After what seemed ages and ages it was time for Vicky to sit for her final examinations. Hours were spent revising and trying to remember years of work. She was sure she would forget everything when the day came. She became a bundle of nerves and could not sleep; long passages from books entered her mind instead. But once she was sitting there in the silent examination room, reading the questions over and over again, the butterflies left her stomach and she began to write the answers. After a week of pure torture it was over. She hoped that she had done well enough and she could now concentrate on something much more important: her birthday party.

The day of the party, 15th September, at last dawned and early in the morning, flowers and presents started to be delivered. At noon the seamstress arrived with the dress which Vicky had chosen in the end. She knew that no-one would have a similar dress to her own because she had rejected all the dresses in fashion and designed one based on an Edwardian wedding dress she had seen in a museum. It was made of cream lace, was high-bodiced, had a long skirt which made her look even slimmer and taller, and was trimmed with pearls. The lace for the dress had been flown specially from Paris, the material as fine as pure gossamer. Her hair would also be arranged with ribbons, pearls and tiny pink flowers by Flo and Milly. Today she would inherit a family heirloom and she was looking forward to all of it.

There were workers everywhere on the estate, erecting a marquee on the lawn in front of Gran's house, setting up tables, arranging the flowers and wiring the fairy lights and Chinese lanterns. The house soon shone, sparkled and looked magnificent. Caterers were arriving with food and with barrels of wine and crates of soft drinks. Tessa herself had been cooking for a whole week. Her masterpiece was the birthday cake, the same colour as Vicky's dress and also decorated with lace and pearls. Vicky was floating on a cloud.

116

'If it's like this today, Rosie, what will it be like when I get married?'

'Do you mean when you marry Roger, Vicky?' Rosie teased. 'You'll have to hire the town hall.'

'Mum has invited all the young men she considers eligible, so who knows, I might choose a prince charming tonight,' laughed Vicky.

Victoria could not have been happier. All of her schoolfriends were coming as well as her relations. Of course Arthur and Ramon were not invited to come to the big house, but all the estate staff were asked to food, drink and music in the barn. Vicky had mentioned to Arthur that she would be visiting the barn just after the midnight toasts in the marquee. He said he would give her his present then.

Vicky could not eat anything for lunch, she was too excited. Having ascertained for the tenth time that her dress, shoes, ribbons and flowers were exactly as she wanted them, she called Rosie to help her open up the presents and arrange them for display in the dining room. Milly and Flo were dealing with all the flowers.

The girls displayed the gifts artistically as if they were in a proper exhibition. There was the portrait of Vicky commissioned by her mother, the photographs of Tornado and Tempest from her uncle and a new bicycle from her aunts. Amongst many items were pictures and books and all sorts of china and glass ornaments.

'Look what Roger has sent me!' exclaimed Vicky.

'Well, if that's not an engagement ring, I'd be very surprised,' said Rosie.

As soon as they thought the last present had been exhibited, another box would be brought for Vicky to open. At last, three tables in horseshoe fashion were covered with the gifts and cards of the senders. In

117

between and on small tables all around the room were arrangements of flowers. The whole display had taken hours to finish. It was now time to go around the house to make sure that everything was ready and awaiting.

By 7 p.m. Vicky was eager to put on her beautiful dress and was helped by the maids. She then had her hair combed and the pearls, ribbons, lace and flowers were pinned amongst her black curls. She looked in the mirror and was satisfied with what she saw. She pirouetted, sending lace and ribbons swirling. Rosie and the rest of the family trooped into the bedroom.

'You look ravishing, Vicky, quite the young lady,' said her uncle.

'Lovely, lovely!' the others concurred.

'Your eyes are sparkling like jewels,' said Rosie. 'How do you do it?'

'There is only one thing missing,' said her grandmother royally, and she gave Uncle Roland a box. Smiling, he opened the velveted jewel box decorated with the family crest and took out a double string of pearls. He picked them up gently and walked forward to fasten them around Vicky's neck. Her family cheered. Victoria looked perfect. It was nearly time to greet the first guests and they all went down to the front door, waiting at the top of the steps.

Her schoolfriends were the first to arrive, dressed in the full flowing skirts which were fashionable at the time. Following them came Suzanne in resplendent red, on the arm of a tall, dark man.

'This is my fiancé, Jeremy Larch,' she introduced proudly.

'Congratulations,' they each said. 'I'm pleased to meet you.'

Gosh! thought Vicky. Suzanne is only sixteen and I know that Jeremy must be twenty six at least. So old

for her, but he is the son of a rich sugar merchant. Well, good luck to her!

Irene and Dr Dumas were coming up the steps and after their greetings Vicky said to Irene, 'Suzanne is here with Jeremy, she is engaged to him.'

'Is she really, at sixteen? I'll be twenty one or twenty two by the time I finish my medical studies, Vicky. I suppose no-one will want to marry such an old maid then.'

'You can have him,' Vicky said indicating Roger who was coming up the steps, followed as usual by Emma and their parents. Irene laughed.

Emma was wearing green taffeta and she did not look comfortable. Kind Rosie came forward whilst Roger was pouncing on Vicky.

'You look beautiful!' he said.

'What a natural colour, Emma,' said Rosie, 'like the green of the forest. You liked the tree house didn't you, perhaps that's why you chose the colour?'

'Maybe Rosie, I don't know. I'm not so sure now that it suits me but if you like it . . . peach does suit you, but then any colour would match with your curly black hair.' Emma relaxed perceptibly.

Once all the guests had arrived and her Gran's house was full, Vicky flitted merrily from group to group chatting, thanking them for the gifts, accepting their compliments, being charming and welcoming to everyone. Then the dance music began, played by a four piece band in one part of the marquee and couples moved across the lawn to dance. Roger grabbed hold of her. 'My dance, DARLING Victoria. You look good enough to eat and I can't wait to marry you,' he was telling her as they danced. She tried to pull away as he was kissing her cheek.

'Remember, Vicky, that we are made for each other.

120

I've told you often enough since we were kids. We've got money, good looks, what else do you want? Just tell me when you are ready and I'll ask for your hand, tonight if you wish, it would be absolutely wonderful.'

'This is my happy day Roger, please don't spoil it. I am very sorry but I do not love you and have no intention of marrying you . . .'

'You will, cousin dear, you will. I'll make you come to your senses.'

Suddenly she wished it was midnight and she could go to the barn.

Instead it was time for the banquet. All the guests sat down in the marquee for the feast. At the end of the five course meal, towards midnight, the band played 'Happy Birthday' and the speeches began, followed by the toasts. For Vicky all this was still enjoyable enough but she was beginning to get restless. As soon as the dancing started again she refused to dance with the young men keen to partner her and instead rounded up the rest of the family and led them to the barn.

The tenants and workers clapped as she came in and surged forward to toast her. She saw Arthur at once in a dark corner, lit up, it seemed, by his golden hair. More presents were given to her and the most senior worker spun her round the barn in an old-fashioned polka. Her family mingled with the staff and dancing resumed in the barn. Vicky made her way to the recess where Arthur was waiting for her. He gave her a small packet and said, 'Open it later. Let's dance now.'

He pulled her in his arms and held her in a gentle embrace. They danced like before, as one, as air. Victoria closed her eyes and let complete contentment wash over her. When the music stopped, Arthur kissed her tenderly on the lips for the first time.

'Happy birthday, I love you,' he murmured.

They suddenly came out of their trance, aware that all noise had stopped in the barn and that eyes were watching them from every corner of the room. The magical spell was broken.

Uncle Roland walked up to Vicky, and ignoring Arthur completely, guided her firmly off the floor, and followed by the rest of the family, out of the building. When they were out of earshot, he said, 'This was disgraceful behaviour, Vicky,' and as the others started to talk, he added, 'Enough! We'll discuss the matter tomorrow. Now it is our duty to rejoin our guests.'

Victoria's wonderful party had come crashing about her ears.

19

The Flight

After the ball, wrath and anger swept over the estate like thundering black clouds. There was indignation at Mrs Benoit for having sons who were tolerated as friends on the estate but forgot their position. There was resentment at Aunts Beatrice and Charlotte for having encouraged the friendship too far with holidays and dancing lessons; outrage at the staff for treating the boys too much as equals and, lastly, great exasperation at the girls for not remembering their proper station in life in relation to the estate employees.

Mrs De Vere went the next day to see Mrs Benoit and in no uncertain terms told her that the friendship between her sons and her own daughters must stop. Mrs Benoit, startled, promised she would talk to her boys but she could not control her tears of dismay. Grandmother and Uncle Roland came to talk to the girls at the villa.

'I warned you,' started Gran De Vere, when Vicky boldly interrupted her.

'Why are you all being so unkind?' she cried. 'You are upsetting everybody. We have done nothing wrong. The boys have been our closest and best friends for three years now.'

'Now, will you please sit down Vicky and listen to me? I can see that we must have some plain speaking and I don't want to be interrupted again. I thought that I had made it quite clear that you have a responsibility to behave as an heir to the De Vere Estate. Perhaps you were too young to understand, so now I must be blunt, dear girl. This friendship is not suitable between you and this poor boy and has gone on long enough. Now it has to end, otherwise Mrs Benoit and her family will be asked to leave the estate,' said her grandmother finally.

'That would be terrible! Why, why?' pleaded Vicky.

'For the simple reason that you are going to lose your reputation, Vicky.' Uncle Roland shook his head sadly. 'And once you lose your reputation because you've been seen to kiss that boy, no-one will want to marry you, not even Roger.'

'Well, that's the end of the matter, we've spelt it out for you,' said her mother. 'I suggest you go to your room and write a kind letter to the boy explaining why your friendship has to end.'

Victoria went to her room and locked herself in. She then opened the drawer where she had hidden Arthur's present to her. She unwrapped the packet he had given her and found a book of love poems. He had written them, printed them and illuminated them as the monks used to do in the past.

'I love you too,' she said clasping the book to her. She thought her heart would break and she cried and cried. For two days she refused food and would not unlock her door. On the third evening Tessa knocked on the door.

'My little girl, my baby, listen, I've told them I'd bring

124

you your favourite broth and bread. Open the door, my pet, as I've got a secret letter for you.'

In a flash Victoria opened the door and hugged Cook, who insisted she ate the food first. Only then did she give her Arthur's letter. She opened the letter with a beating heart.

Darling Vicky,

Bad news I'm afraid. Mum has seen Prior Jules and they are planning to transfer me to the other monastery. Thank goodness I'll be able to continue to learn printing there too.

All the adults say that we must stop being friends. To me, they say frankly that as you are a rich girl, I am no better than a fortune hunter. What they mean is that there is a money barrier between us, you are on one side of the reef and I am on the other side.

Can we meet once more to say goodbye? If it is not possible, I want you to remember that I shall always love you and if you ever need your best friend I'll be there.

All my love,
Arthur

Quickly she replied and gave her answer to Tessa to forward to Arthur.

Dear Arthur,

Come on, let's show all these people who want to separate us that we do not want to be separated. The only way to do this, I fear, is to go away together. When they find out what our friendship means to us, they will leave us alone and we'll be as we were before. After all aren't they supposed

125

to love us and wish the best for us?

Tomorrow night when everyone is asleep, I'll sneak out and borrow the station wagon. Come behind the sugar factory; with the noise there, nobody will hear us. I'll take an overnight bag and Tessa is giving me food to take. See what you can bring too.

Your loving,
Vicky

New emotions flowed through Vicky that she never thought she had. At last she fell into a fitful sleep as plans and hopes began to emerge in her mind.

The following night, like lovers, they met and embraced.

'Where are we going?' asked Arthur.

'Remember the slaves who found refuge on Mournful Rock? I think we should follow their example.' She took command as usual.

They drove in silence for the rest of the night until they were near enough to the Rock. They hid the car in the forest and set off, carrying what they had brought with them. There were more footholds and roots to grab than in the time of the slaves. But it was still not easy to climb and haul their packages with them. Eventually they found a small cave in which to shelter. During two days they lived blissfully, pushing to the back of their minds that soon their idyll would be over and they would have to return to reality. Only once did Vicky say, 'Pray God they realise how strongly we feel for each other and how we value our friendship.'

On the third day the promise of a storm was in the air and they went out to the edge of the cliff together. The sun became submerged in cheerless clouds. As the sky darkened, the waves down below were pushed up by giant hands and then crashed down with ferocity. Victoria watched them heap up again and again before toppling into foam.

'Don't be frightened,' Arthur said calmly. 'An electric storm is brewing over the ocean. It's going to pour with rain in any minute; we'll have to get back to the cave or get drenched.'

Sure enough, flashes of lightning forked across the sky and there was an explosive rumble. Bullets of hail hit the rock and attacked their heads as they hurried as quickly as possible towards the small cave. They huddled together in the entrance whilst the rain came down, making the rock as shiny and slippery as polished marble.

By afternoon the rain eased off and they were able to emerge from their shelter. Life no longer seemed so rosy and comfortable. Looking into the distance Arthur pointed to some activity along the shore.

'That's the end of it, Arthur,' said Vicky unhappily. 'Tessa must have become worried and given them a clue. It's over, but I can't say I am sorry to leave this place.'

'No,' replied Arthur. 'We are running out of food and dry clothes. All right let's go down and face the music.'

'Do you think our plan will work, that they will understand and let us stay as we were before all this?' asked Vicky wistfully.

'I hope so, I hope so,' he answered.

For a while they held each other tightly and kissed. Then they picked up their bags and filled them with their bits and pieces before making their way warily down the greasy path. Tears were blurring Victoria's eyes and spilling down her cheeks.

Suddenly, bounding round the bend came Moses full

of hysterical joy at seeing them. What happened next happened with dreadful and fatal speed. Victoria made to pat and greet the dog. She slipped and started to fall, pushing Moses away from her. Arthur, close behind, grabbed her arm. They both tried to steady themselves, lost their balance, swayed for a second and then fell . . . fell . . . crashing onto the rocks below. One scream of despair rent the air, then silence as a great tunnel of boiling, churning water engulfed them completely.

They died instantly.

It was the worst tragedy the island had experienced for a long time. The families were devastated and could not be consoled. Only time managed to mend their hearts.

Since that fateful day, whenever a cyclone threatens the island and the sailors and fishermen make for safety, many have claimed to have seen the friends embracing on the rocks and they hear their voices carried as wisps of the wind.

'They sound happy,' they say. 'In death they've stayed friends eternally.'

Epilogue

Ironically, within ten years of the friends' deaths, prejudices related to wealth, class, colour and religion had diminished on the island. This was due mainly to greater links with the rest of the world at the end of the Second World War. The islanders became better educated and more broad-minded.

The De Vere estate was plunged into despair by the double tragedy. Not long afterwards Gran De Vere died, of a broken heart it was said. Mrs Benoit became the companion of Vicky's mother. They comforted each other and found some solace.

Rosie, when she finished school, decided to go to a training college to qualify as a teacher. She was determined to give a better education to the small children on the estate.

Ramon, who had always been good at maths, was offered a scholarship by the monks to go to university abroad to study accountancy. The monks hoped he would then return to work for them, but he refused the offer. 'No thank you,' he said. 'I can stay here and learn accounting from Monk André. He needs me now. He's nearly blind and I can't leave my mother and . . .' he stopped short before saying, 'Rosie.'

So he started an apprenticeship at the Monastery instead.

After two years Rosie had qualified and was back home. She and Ramon were walking in Gran's garden when Ramon said to her, 'I really should go to town and work in a bank now that I have learnt everything I can here at the Monastery.'

She questioned him and listened to his plans. That evening she went to talk to Uncle Roland.

'Uncle, Ramon thinks he ought to leave the estate and work in town to further his career. I don't want him to go. I'm going to ask him to marry me instead and work on the estate if that's all right with you. You keep saying you can't find good staff these days and you don't trust anyone to do the accounts. I know Ramon won't ask me to marry him even after all the years we've been friends and then loved each other. So I'll have to propose. Do you know, Uncle, that Roger came to see me twice at college and asked me to marry him? Poor Roger, he was convinced he would get De Vere Domaine through Vicky. About Ramon . . .'

'How times have changed! Not only you wanting to marry a poor boy after what's happened, but actually being prepared to ask him. As your husband he would, of course, have his own rights on this estate, but if that is what you wish, so be it,' Uncle Roland told her.

Rosie and Ramon were married in a quiet ceremony on the De Vere Domaine. Only close relations and the employees were present.

Eventually their children inherited the De Vere Domaine.

As for Moses, he attached himself more closely to Rosie, and when she was away, to Ramon. But he was never quite as boisterous as before. He was for ever cocking his head and listening, perhaps hoping to hear the tread of the friends' feet. During storms when the wind whistled, he would go near the door, waiting for it to open and let Victoria and Arthur come in.

He never learnt!